PENUMBRA

THE TIDE OF YEARS

an adventure module for characters of 4th to 6th level

BY MICHELLE A. BROWN NEPHEW

CONTENTS

THE TIDE OF YEARS

CREDITS

AUTHOR: Michelle A. Brown Nephew
EDITING, DEVELOPMENT & INTERIOR LAYOUT: John Nephew
EDITORIAL ASSISTANCE: Alex Knapik
ORIGINAL PENUMBRA COVER DESIGN: John Tynes
COVER ILLUSTRATION: Helena Wickberg, Phoenix Studios
INTERIOR GRAPHIC DESIGN, ART DIRECTION, AND
  CARTOGRAPHY: Scott Reeves
INTERIOR ILLUSTRATIONS: Ross Bonilla, David Interdonato, Scott Reeves,
  Chris Seaman, Helena Wickberg
PLAYTESTING: Sara Bebus, Matthew Budde, Jeramie Cooper, Rebecca Hauck,
  Michael Hills, Alex Knapik, Zach Lutterman, Kevin Luebke, John Nephew, Kevin
  Ohland, Jeff Peterson, Jon Peterson, Amanda Rhode, Dave Risk, AJ Schmockel,
  Mat Tugas

ABOUT THE AUTHOR

Although she's been a committed gamer for almost a decade, Michelle A. Brown Nephew has only recently burst into the RPG publishing scene. She is now the Line Editor for Penumbra and several other Atlas projects, when not teaching English at the University of Wisconsin — River Falls. Her previous writing credits include one hardbound copy of a masters thesis hidden away in the bowels of West Virginia University's library, and some really bad high school poetry.

PO BOX 131233 • ROSEVILLE, MN 55113
INFO@ATLAS-GAMES.COM • WWW.ATLAS-GAMES.COM

FIRST PRINTING • MARCH 2001
ISBN 1-887801-98-7

CHAPTER ONE
THE SPIRIT OF LAGUEEN

Lost in the darkness of legend is the story of a land left to perish by its own hand, whose ultimate source of power became its final demise.

Here was a people of learning and magic, whose talent lay in harnessing the flow of time itself. By peering into the future, and even moving backward into time to glean the lost secrets of fallen nations, the people of Lagueen had access to the technology and knowledge of the ages. They learned a lesson from the extinct empires they encountered, avoiding their own end through war or want by becoming self-sustaining and content within their limited realm.

By pooling the temporal energy of the people of Lagueen, time became a servant of the combined will of a nation. Harsh winters shortened and brief growing seasons lasted months longer, allowing harvests unparalleled in history — even floods were foreseen and prepared against. They limited their numbers to what the valley could tolerate, and with the exception of a few malcontent young people, were at ease with nature and themselves.

All this was possible because of the existence of an object of untold power, the Temporal Crystal. Guarded by the priests of Ras'Tan, the Crystal was the repository of the nation's temporal energy. At birth, children were taken to the temple pyramid to be dedicated to Ras'Tan, and to add their energy to that of their ancestors before them. The Crystal was used for the good of all for centuries on end, and Lagueen became the jewel of the known world.

But even in the midst of prosperity and plenty, ambition and self-service can breed in the dark corners of the human spirit. This was proven when one night an acolyte at the temple of Ras'Tan crept into the Temporal Chamber. As she struggled to dislodge the Crystal from its centuries-long resting place on the altar to her people's god, a young priest happened upon the theft, and called an alarm. With dozens of her brethren filling the room and nowhere to turn, the desperate thief's only thought was escape to a place beyond the reach of Ras'Tan and his followers. The young priest grabbed the corner of her robe, just as the thief's desire triggered the Crystal and all the power contained therein. In an instant thief, priest, and Crystal blinked out of time, never to be seen again by the people of Lagueen.

Without the Crystal, the city-state of Lagueen languished quickly, and within a decade it was no more. Once-majestic buildings crumbled and were engulfed by the surrounding forest. Terraced fields withered and died, and the rains carried rich topsoil down the hillsides into the river to be washed away. Finally, with no one left to maintain them, the terraces could hold no more — a landslide ripped across the face of the bluffs, blocking the end of the river valley. The river bloated and the valley floor flooded, covering the remains of Lagueen in a shroud of murky waters.

All that is left of Lagueen are rumors of its spent greatness, and echoes of its lost power …

ADVENTURE OVERVIEW

This adventure is designed for four to six players, using characters of 4th to 6th level. It should be playable in one six-hour session, or split into two shorter sessions by saving Chapter Three and on — the underwater segments — for another day.

The emphasis in this module is not necessarily on combat, but rather on the Player Characters (PCs) completing several thought puzzles in order to accomplish their goal. In fact, there is no "bad guy" for them to destroy (although there are, of course, some pretty dangerous monsters). Instead, the PCs must find a way to breach the underwater pyramid, traverse the temple while it is distorted by temporal disturbances, and finally send the Crystal back to its original time. This adventure is also designed as a segue to further adventures in time for the PCs, as the Game Moderator (GM) has the option of extending the scenario into the characters' personal histories or beyond.

CC2 MAPS

The maps in this module were created using *Campaign Cartographer 2* from ProFantasy Software. The PC-format files of these maps are available on our website; just point your browser at **www.atlas-games.com**. If you own *Campaign Cartographer 2*, you can download these maps and use or manipulate them as you see fit, linking them into your own campaign maps, modifying them to integrate with your campaign world, and so forth. Even if you don't own *CC2*, you can follow a link on our site to the ProFantasy website, **www.profantasy.com**, where you can download a free map reader.

OPEN GAMING CONTENT

The Penumbra™ line of D20 System™ supplements is published under the terms of the D20 System Trademark License and the Open Gaming License. The portions of this book which are rules-related — for example, character statistics and monster descriptions — are defined as open gaming content.

OGC Boxes

To clearly distinguish the Open Gaming Content in this module from the rest of the material we have placed Open Gaming Content in boxes like this one.

This means that you are welcome to borrow and use these materials, under the terms of the Open Gaming License (see the Appendix for its detailed terms), in materials of your own creation. For example, you could use a new spell from this adventure for a different adventure that you design and share with the rest of the world through your personal website, or even in a printed publication. The open gaming content is contained in the parchment-backed insert boxes throughout this book.

The artwork in this adventure and most of the original storyline text does not rely on the D20 system, and thus is not open gaming content. This material, which is everything outside of the insert boxes, cannot be reproduced in any way without the express permission of Atlas Games or the individual artist who owns the copyright to the image.

As we go to press with this adventure, the D20 System Trademark License, although nearly finalized, is still in draft form. If you are interested in doing Open Gaming License or D20 System products of your own, you should go to **www.opengamingfoundation.org** on the World Wide Web to find the current status and latest versions of the licenses.

ENTER THE CHARACTERS

The characters come into the story as they are traveling through a dense woods. They may be on their way to a distant city to attend the wedding of dear friends, to resupply after a long stretch of dungeon crawling, to attend the local festival, or whatever suits your story line thus far. Having set up camp near the southern bank of a large lake, the party spends an uneventful night until dawn.

Especially perceptive nature types, such as rangers and druids, might notice a certain strangeness to the surrounding forest. This will cause them to be uneasy without quite knowing

ILLUSTRATION BY DAVID INTERDONATO

why. They may wake several times during the night to an undefined feeling of "wrongness."

> If they try making Spot checks (DC 10), the PCs may notice that this section of the forest seems unnaturally ancient compared to the young woods they traversed through most of the day. Druids make this roll automatically.

Immense trees and giant ferns lurk in the darkness, and an odd stillness presides over the night. Just before dawn, an impressive sixteen-point stag stumbles into the camp, probably meaning to drink at the lake. It quickly leaps back into the surrounding blackness when it notices the characters.

As the sun rises above the hills, the character on guard spots movement in the underbrush.

> If there is no posted sentry, the PC with the highest Intelligence spots the movement.

After being hailed by the characters, a man of about thirty years makes his way into the camp and asks to join the group. He is a dark-complexioned human and wears a yellow sari-like robe that implies his status as a cleric, although no one in the group would be able to identify the sect he owes allegiance to from either his appearance or garb. He introduces himself to the PCs, telling them his name is Jonar and that he is a priest of Ras'Tan, of the Lagueen nation.

> At this point, the use of *legend lore* or an appropriate Knowledge skill (DC 15; DC 10 for human characters) can reveal an abbreviated history of Lagueen.

PCs who succeed on their roll know that this was an ancient civilization devoted to knowledge and learning, which fell into decline when a powerful artifact was stolen from its holy temple. Human children are told the story of Lagueen as a warning against selfishness and tendencies toward theft. Several of the characters may not find mention of Jonar's homeland familiar, but he proceeds to ask the characters for their help.

THE MYSTERIOUS STRANGER

Jonar is not as he appears. He is, in fact, the undead spirit of the young priest come back to right the theft of the Temporal Crystal.

The thief's last-ditch triggering of the Temporal Crystal did deliver her — and Jonar as a tagalong — from the priests of Ras'Tan, but she didn't take into proper consideration what the effects of the theft would be on the far future she was about to become a part of herself.

As an acolyte she was used to the idea that the future was open to travelers from her own time. But for the people of Lagueen time was necessarily a mutable force dependent on their use of the Crystal; the thief's criminal actions were her nation's death sentence, forming a new time line never before encountered by the priests of Ras'Tan. The priests' temple has fallen into ruin at the bottom of a lake bed as a consequence, and the Crystal manipulates only time, not space. The Crystal transported both thief and young priest to a time beyond the reaches of the priests of Ras'Tan, but she and Jonar drowned upon their arrival.

Jonar does not entirely comprehend the significance of his new non-corporeal state. He regained awareness on the banks of the lake at sunrise, and soon came to the conclusion that he is now in a time other than his own. After orienting himself to his new situation, Jonar determined that centuries had passed since the theft, but he remained confused as to the changes in the landscape around him. He recognized a few of the natural landmarks as being those of his homeland, but where was the great capital of Lagueen? Where were its soaring towers and broad boulevards filled with the city's citizens? Finally, he forced himself to accept the truth of the downfall of his people, and resolved not to rest until he can restore the glory of Lagueen.

Provoking the Priest

Jonar is not aware of the new special attacks he possesses as a ghost, such as *corrupting touch* and *telekinesis*. His desire to save his people triggered manifestation, but he does not have any control over this ability. Similarly, an attempt to attack an opponent might result in the inadvertent use of *corrupting touch,* and *telekinesis* would kick in to move an object out of his way if he was distracted enough not to remember he is incorporeal. In both of these cases, Jonar would forget that he is intangible and try to accomplish these things through physical contact. Special qualities such as *rejuvenation* and *turn resistance* are activated by unique circumstances, so he may never realize he has these abilities.

If they refuse to help him too often, Jonar will try to use *command* to force the PC he perceives to be the leader of the group of adventurers into following him through the forest to find the Shard or Kyrielee (see the next chapter). He might also try to use *calm emotions* to subdue the characters, thinking that they will be more open-minded if he can settle things down again. If this doesn't work, he may become violent and somewhat irrational in his desperation to convince them. In this case he will use *searing light* (dealing 4d8 damage) to blind the most troublesome PC, showing him "the light of truth which harms only those who wallow in the darkness of cowardice and fear." However, remember that Jonar really doesn't want injure the characters — after all, he still needs them. If things get too heated, he'll just leave and try convincing them again in about a half hour — and every half hour after that if need be.

If the characters try to attack him, remember that Jonar can only be harmed by +1 or better magic weapons, spells, spell-like abilities, or supernatural abilities, and has a 50 percent chance to ignore even these attacks when from a corporeal source. A priest of Ras'Tan is not an opponent to be taken lightly, especially after his death.

Jonar, Cleric of Ras'Tan

Undead 8th-Level Cleric, Incorporeal

Hit Dice:	8d12+2 (50 hp)
Initiative:	−1
Speed:	Fly 30 ft. (perfect)
AC:	12 (when manifested; +3 deflection bonus)/9 (during ethereal encounters)
Attacks:	Dagger (melee) +8/+3 (affects ethereal creatures only, masterwork)
Damage:	Dagger (melee) 1d4
Face/Reach:	5 ft. by 5 ft./5 ft.
Special Attacks:	Manifestation, corrupting touch, telekinesis, turn undead
Special Qualities:	Rejuvenation, turn resistance, undead immunities
Saves:	Fort +9, Ref +2, Will +10
Abilities:	Str 13, Dex 8, Con —, Int 10, Wis 17, Cha 16
Skills:	Spellcraft +11, Concentration +13, Scry +6, Knowledge (history) +6, Heal +6, Diplomacy +6, Listen +8, Hide +8, Search +8, Spot +8
Feats:	Scribe Scroll, Brew Potion, Combat Casting
Deity/Domains:	Ras'Tan/Sun and Time
Languages:	Common, Celestial, Temporal
Challenge Rating:	10
Treasure:	masterwork dagger, pouch with 10 gp (on body; incorporeal on ghost)
Alignment:	Neutral Good

Cleric Spells & Abilities

Non-Domain Spells Per Day: 6/5/4/4/2

Prepared Cleric Spells:

0 Level: *detect magic, *detect temporal disturbance, **guidance, mending, read magic, **resistance*

1st Level: *bless, cause fear, command, doom, summon monster I*

2nd Level: *calm emotions, *dispel temporal effect, hold person, spiritual weapon (scimitar)*

3rd Level: *dispel magic, prayer, summon monster III, wind wall*

4th Level: *sending, summon monster IV*
* Signifies a new cleric spell described on pp. 9-12.
** Since he is incorporeal, these touch-range spells will most likely only be usable on Jonar himself

Time Domain Granted Power: Ability to cast Time domain spells at +1 caster level (see Time Domain insert page 9).

Prepared Time Domain Spells: *true strike, haste* (see New Cleric Spells insert, page pp. 9-12).

Sun Domain Granted Power: Can use greater turning instead of regular turning once per day.

Prepared Sun Domain Spells: *searing light, fire shield*

Turn Undead: Up to four times each day.

Undead Special Attacks & Special Qualities

Manifestation (Su): Jonar is only able to manifest only when the sun is visible.

Corrupting Touch (Su): Deals a living target 1d4 damage, with −1 modifier to attack roll. Deals incorporeal target 1d4+1 damage, with +1 modifier to attack roll.

Telekinesis (Su): Can use once per round as an 8th-level sorcerer.

Rejuvenation (Su): Restores self in 2d4 days.

Turn Resistance (Ex): +4 turn resistance.

Undead Immunities (Su): Jonar is immune to poison, sleep, paralysis, stunning, disease, death effects, necromantic effects, and mind-influencing effects. He is also not subject to critical hits, subdual damage, ability damage, ability drain, energy drain, or any effects that require a Fortitude save.

Incorporeal: Can only be harmed by incorporeal creatures, +1 or better magic weapons, spells, spell-like abilities, and supernatural abilities. When hit by spells or magic weapons, there is a 50% chance of ignoring damage from a corporeal source.

NEW GOD:
Ras'Tan the All-Knower

Alignment: Neutral Good

Domains: Sun, Time, Knowledge

Typical Worshipers: Citizens of the nation of Lagueen, and those who have had contact with them; those who encounter temporal disturbances or who have themselves been displaced in time; those entering the last 1/3 of their lifespan.

Description: The god of the nation of Lagueen, Ras'Tan (ross-*tahn*) is Neutral Good. His title is the All-Knower, or the Seer. He is

the god of enlightenment, and favors those possessed of wisdom gained through experience and age. He rewards innovation and discovery in the arts and sciences, and the preservation of history. Though his followers are few, those who are true to his ways find a power that comes only with the knowledge of ages. Because they are relatively unknown to the rest of the world, his priests are often mistaken for those of other sun gods. The domains he is associated with are Sun, Time, and Knowledge. His favored weapon is the scimitar.

ILLUSTRATION BY SCOTT REEVES

PLAYING THE GHOST-CLERIC

At this point in the adventure, Jonar has not been confronted with the reality of his death; he believes he managed somehow to swim up through the apex of the pyramid in the Temporal Chamber before losing consciousness. Because of this, he will act completely human at all times; no floating through walls or fading out to translucence for him. On the other hand, he no longer experiences hunger or fatigue, and so will not eat or sleep. Also remember that he is an incorporeal presence, and as such cannot touch anything of the mortal plane.

After the sun goes down, Jonar is no longer able to maintain even this limited visual aspect; as a former sun priest, what power he has left is now dependent on that glowing orb's presence in the sky. He has noticed this, of course, but has convinced himself that it is a result of the temporal shift combined with the loss of the Crystal — he thinks that he is just slightly out of phase with the current timeline because the acolyte used the Crystal improperly in her desperation, and believes that restoring the Crystal is the only way to restore his solid form, as well as regaining his friends, family, and nation.

As a precaution against revealing his incorporeal nature, Jonar avoids tactile contact with others. He believes that hiding his condition from the characters may help him stay in favor with them, so he conceals the fact that he cannot hold

or carry anything other than what he had on his person at the time of his death. If anyone in the party notices this, he will give the excuse he has made for himself: temporal displacement.

If the players disbelieve this explanation or become accusatory, allow them to roll their Sense Motive skill; Jonar truly believes his story and has only good intentions, a successful roll against a Hunch DC of 20 reveals this fact.

The only thing that will shake Jonar out of this belief is seeing his own dead body.

Jonar knows the history of the Lagueen up to his own disappearance, and has constructed the rest from the evidence at hand. He is more than willing to tell the PCs all that he knows in order to convince them to help him, and he will offer them the thanks of a nation as reward. If the PCs are of a more mercenary inclination, Jonar might at this point mention the glorious treasures of Lagueen no doubt preserved beneath the water's surface in their temple.

The ghost of the priest has imprinted himself on the PCs as the first people he encountered after regaining consciousness; he is haunting them, in effect. He will not leave them alone until they agree to help him regain the Crystal and put things aright; this means swimming to the bottom of the lake, entering the temple, finding the crystal, and triggering it to return to its home time.

NEW CLERICAL DOMAIN:

Time

Deity: Ras'Tan

Favored Language: Temporal

Granted Power: Clerics choosing the Time domain cast time spells at +1 caster level.

The spells associated with this new Domain have been carefully chosen so as not to unbalance a game by giving lower-level characters direct access to the powerful forces of time travel. Those secrets are reserved for only the most learned of Ras'Tan's priests and are jealously guarded by them. However, any character who comes into contact with the effects of time manipulation, and so begins to understand how the currents of time can be changed to benefit human(-oid)kind, may gain the connection to needed to devote himself to the mysteries of the Time Domain. This means that a PC who completes this adventure is free to multiclass as a cleric devoted to Ras'Tan, taking Time as one of his Domains (see "Typical Worshipers" in the "New God" insert to the left).

Time Domain Spells

1   **True Strike.** Gain +20 insight bonus into your next single attack roll.

2   **Haste.** Subject takes an extra partial action and gains +4 haste bonus to AC.

3   **Slow.** Subject takes only a partial action each turn and suffers –2 penalties to AC, melee attack rolls, melee damage rolls, and Reflex saves.

4   **Scry the Ages.** You can see and hear some creature, who may be at any distance or in any time frame past or future. (See description on page 10)

5   **Hastening of Age.** The subject loses Str, Dex, and Con levels as his body ages prematurely. (See description on page 11)

6   **Mass Haste.** As haste, but it affects multiple creatures.

7   **Wellspring of Youth.** The subject gains Str, Dex, and Con levels as his body regains its youth. (See description on page 12)

8   **Time Stop.** You are free to act for 1d4+1 rounds of apparent time while time ceases to flow for everyone else.

9   **Temporal Stasis.** Time ceases to flow for the subject, who is in an impenetrable state of suspended animation.

New Cleric Spells

DETECT TEMPORAL DISTURBANCE

Universal [Time]
Level: Clr 0, Sor/Wiz 0
Components: V, S
Casting Time: 1 action
Range: 60 ft.
Area: Quarter circle emanating from you to the extreme of the range
Duration: Concentration, up to 1 minute/level (D)
Saving Throw: None
Spell Resistance: No

You can sense the presence of a disturbance in the natural flow of time up to 60 feet away in your own time frame. This includes the use of spells that manipulate time in any way, natural temporal distortions or gateways, objects that are displaced from their original time, and temporal creatures such as the time elemental described on page 41). The amount of information revealed depends on how long you study a particular area, as in the *detect magic* spell.

1st Round: You can detect the presence or absence of temporal disturbances.

2nd Round: Number of different temporal disturbances and the amount of time between the

origin and current temporal position of the most powerful disturbance.

3rd Round: The location and amount of time between the origin and current temporal position of each temporal disturbance. If the disturbances are in line of sight, you can make multiple Spellcraft skill checks to determine the exact nature of the temporal disturbances; this would include information such as the caster level and type of spell, or the type and level of the creature.

Note: Each round you can turn to detect things in a new area. The spell can penetrate barriers, but one foot of stone, one inch of common metal, a thin sheet of lead, or three feet of wood or dirt blocks it.

DISPEL TEMPORAL EFFECT

Abjuration [Time]
Level: Clr 2, Sor/Wiz 2
Components: V, S
Casting Time: 1 action
Range: Medium (100 ft. + 10 ft./level)
Target or Area: One temporal effect
Duration: Instantaneous
Saving Throw: None
Spell Resistance: No

The caster can dispel any spell cast on a creature or object that manipulates time (such as *haste*, *time stop*, *temporal stasis*, or *slow*) or has "time" as a descriptor (such as the new cleric spells described in this section), causing it to end as if its duration had expired. It can also suppress the time-related abilities of a magic item, temporarily close an individual temporal disturbance such as a temporal gateway or time distortion (like the time traps listed on pages 39-40), or dissipate a creature relying on an ongoing time spell for its presence (such as the time elemental described on page 41). In addition, it is able to counter another spellcaster's time spell, or to dispel the ongoing effects of supernatural abilities and spell-like effects that manipulate time. This spell can be used as a targeted dispel or counterspell, like the *dispel magic* spell:

Targeted Dispel: The target is one object, creature, temporal disturbance, or time spell. The caster of *dispel temporal effect* makes a dispel check against the time spell or against each ongoing time spell currently affecting the object or creature. Instantaneous spells cannot be affected, since the magical process is already over before *dispel temporal effect* can be cast. The dispel check is 1d20 +1 per caster level, to a maximum of +10, against a DC of 11 + the spell's caster level. If the spellcaster targets an object or creature who is the effect of an ongoing time spell (such as the time elemental in this adventure), he makes a dispel check to end the time spell that conjured the object or creature. If the object targeted is a magic item, the caster makes a dispel check against the item's caster level. If the roll succeeds, all the item's time-related properties are suppressed for 1d4 rounds, after which the item recovers on its own. A time portal or other ongoing temporal distortion (such as a time trap) is temporarily closed in this same manner. You automatically succeed at your dispel check against any time spell that you cast yourself.

Counterspell: The spell targets a spellcaster and is cast as a counterspell. Unlike a true counterspell, however, the caster of *dispel temporal effect* must make a dispel check to counter the other spellcaster's time spell.

SCRY THE AGES

Divination [Time]
Level: Clr 6, Sor/Wiz 5, Time 4
Components: V, S, M/DF, F
Casting Time: 1 hour
Range: See text
Effect: Magical sensor
Duration: 1 minute/level
Saving Throw: None
Spell Resistance: No

As in the spell *scrying*, this spell allows the cleric to see and hear a creature at any distance, but also in any period of time past or future (the time must be specified by the caster beforehand). The DC depends on how well the caster knows the subject and the type of physical connection he has to the person or creature.

Knowledge	DC
None	20
Secondhand	15
Firsthand	10
Familiar	5

Effects of Hastening of Age

		+3 Str, Con, & Dex	–1 Str, Con, & Dex	–2 Str, Con, & Dex	–3 Str, Con, & Dex
Race	**Childhood**	**Adulthood**	**Middle Age**	**Old Age**	**Venerable Age**
Human	7 years	15 years	35 years	53 years	70 years
Dwarf	20 years	40 years	125 years	188 years	250 years
Elf	55 years	110 years	175 years	263 years	350 years
Gnome	20 years	40 years	100 years	150 years	200 years
Half-elf	10 years	20 years	62 years	93 years	125 years
Half-orc	7 years	14 years	30 years	45 years	60 years
Halfling	10 years	20 years	50 years	75 years	100 years

Connection	Scry Check Bonus
Likeness	+5
Possession	+8
Body Part	+10

Creatures with an Intelligence of 12 or higher can make a Scry skill check (or Intelligence check) against DC 20 to notice the magical sensor generated by the spell. Spells (except *message*) can be cast through the *scry the ages* spell as specified for the *scry* spell.

Arcane Material Components: A jewelry "eye" fashioned of a diamond set in gold, with a minimum cost of 250 gp, which vanishes upon being cast into the focus when the spell is cast.

Cleric Focus: A holy water font costing not less than 100 gp.

Sorcerer or Wizard Focus: A mirror of finely wrought and highly polished silver costing not less than 1,000 gp. The mirror must measure at least two feet by four feet.

HASTENING OF AGE

Necromancy [Time]
Level: Clr 7, Sor/Wiz 7, Time 5
Components: V, S
Casting Time: 1 action
Range: Close (25 ft. + 5 ft./2 levels)
Effect: Ray of negative temporal energy
Duration: Instantaneous
Saving Throw: Fortitude negates (see text)
Spell Resistance: Yes

Used as a directed attack, the creature struck ages at an extremely rapid rate — cells degrade and bones turn brittle before their time. The victim of this attack ages one step as per the chart above; his Strength, Constitution, and Dexterity are modified the amount specified above his new age. A character's ability score cannot be reduced below 1 in this way. Undergoing *hastening of age* multiple times produces cumulative affects, but casting the spell on a character of Venerable Age changes him only cosmetically; the spell cannot kill. When aged in this way, you may feel and look older, but the time allotted to your soul remains the same; for instance, though an Adult human character is now Middle Aged for all intents and purposes, he still has his full original 55+2d20 years left to live. Note that the bonuses to Intelligence, Wisdom, and Charisma given to normally aging characters do not apply to this spell, as the target doesn't undergo the experiences that would add to these abilities.

Much like *energy drain*, *hastening of age* requires that twenty-four hours after the attack the subject must make a Fortitude saving throw (using the spell DC) to negate the effects. If he fails, the damage to his abilities and his apparent age become permanent. Success means that the effects begin to fade away. The permanent reduction to a character's ability scores can be dispelled by *restoration*, but not *lesser restoration*; it is a permanent ability drain. *Wellspring of youth* can also counteract it (see next page). *Hastening of age* can only affect mortal creatures that suffer the affects of normal aging; undead creatures and the like are immune.

Effects of Wellspring of Youth

		+3 Str, Con, & Dex	+2 Str, Con, & Dex	+1 Str, Con, & Dex	−3 Str, Con, & Dex
Race	**Venerable Age**	**Old Age**	**Middle Age**	**Adulthood**	**Childhood**
Human	70 years	53 years	35 years	15 years	7 years
Dwarf	250 years	188 years	125 years	40 years	20 years
Elf	350 years	263 years	175 years	110 years	55 years
Gnome	200 years	150 years	100 years	40 years	20 years
Half-elf	125 years	93 years	62 years	20 years	10 years
Half-orc	60 years	45 years	30 years	14 years	7 years
Halfling	100 years	75 years	50 years	20 years	10 years

WELLSPRING OF YOUTH

Conjuration (Healing) [Time]
Level: Clr 8, Time 7
Components: V, S, M, XP
Casting Time: 1 action
Range: Touch
Target: Creature touched
Duration: Instantaneous
Saving Throw: Will negates (harmless)
Spell Resistance: Yes (harmless)

Directed at a single target, this spell allows one person to regain his youth at a rapid rate — cells repair themselves, and wrinkled skin regains its youthful firmness and glow. The recipient of this spell becomes one aging step younger as per the chart above; his Strength, Constitution, and Dexterity are modified the amount specified above his new age. A character's ability score cannot be reduced below 1 in this way. Undergoing *wellspring of youth* multiple times produces cumulative affects, but casting the spell on a character of Childhood age changes him only cosmetically;

the spell cannot kill and is not able to undo death. When aged in this way, you may feel and look younger, but the time allotted to your soul remains the same; for instance, though a Middle Aged human character is now the Adult age of 15 years for most intents and purposes, he still has only his original 35+2d20 years left to live. Although this spell doesn't provide immortality, it is very popular with the wealthy classes as a way to preserve beauty and vigor throughout a lifetime.

Wellspring of youth works to counteract the effects of *hastening of age*, as mentioned above. It can only affect mortal creatures that suffer the affects of normal aging; undead creatures and the like are immune.

Note that an unwilling target (such as an adult who does not wish to be reduced to a child's body in the middle of combat) is entitled to a Will saving throw, if he or she so chooses.

Material Component: Diamond dust worth 100 gp that is sprinkled over the target.

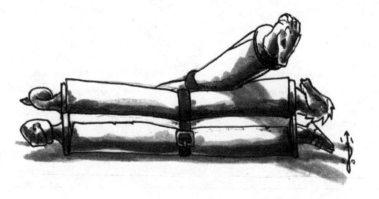

ILLUSTRATION BY ROSS BONILLA

CHAPTER TWO
PREPARATIONS

Once the PCs have decided to help Jonar, they need to be outfitted for the encounter. Unfortunately, they are still several days from the nearest town, so going on a buying spree at the local Spells 'R' Us outlet isn't feasible. If the players seem inclined to force the issue, Jonar will point out the effects the theft of the Crystal is having on the forest, which is beginning to look positively Paleozoic. There really isn't time for a week-long trek to reach civilization.

There are a few things Jonar can do to help prepare them, though. First of all, unless they want to try the old breathing out of a waterskin trick (good luck), they need to be able to breathe underwater. Fortunately, Jonar has already encountered a somewhat less than endearing nixie named Kyrielee who would be able to provide them with this ability, should they be able to win her over.

Jonar also has an intimate knowledge of the temple's floorplans, and so knows where the party might find useful items, magical and otherwise. Descriptions of the rooms in the temple are given on pages 31-37 and a map can be found on the center spread of this booklet, pages 24-25. remember that Jonar wouldn't be able to draw a sketch of the temple for the characters, so the players shouldn't be shown the map until they enter the sunken pyramid.

In particular, Jonar might mention the potions stored in the Laboratories, which include such useful things as a *swimming* potion, a potion of *water breathing*, and an *endurance* potion to aid in making checks for water pressure damage. He will also direct them to the Library where they might find a useful scroll or two.

Finally, Jonar knows that the pyramid is designed to function as a sun clock on a monumental scale. When the Crystal is positioned at the apex of the pyramid, it redirects the sun's rays to a series of smaller crystals spaced at regular intervals around the base of the pyramid. These smaller crystals, called Temporal Shards, are located at an average distance of about 200 feet from the top of the temple, and are themselves reservoirs of temporal energy (see the insert on page 18). Jonar knows that one Shard, in particular, was embedded in a stone cliff-face that is still above water on the southwest wall of the valley. He will suggest that the party retrieve the Shard to give them some defense against the temporal energy that's obviously affecting the area. As an added bonus, the Shard will act as a key to open the temple doors.

DINOSAURS IN THE MIST

When making their way through the forest, all of the characters should now easily notice the change to the woods since they made camp yesterday evening. The uncontrolled temporal energy emanating from the Crystal beneath the lake has transformed the area; now the darkest of ancient broad-leafed evergreens measuring in the hundreds of feet loom overhead, forming a continuous canopy while giant ferns rule the misty forest floor. Unnaturally large winged insects hover over ponderous spore pods and small creatures rustle in the moist foliage of what is now closer to a temperate rainforest than the young woods the party traveled through yesterday.

The characters may come upon several rather odd creatures making their home in this now primeval forest. These can be rolled for as random encounters whenever the GM sees fit, but at least one should occur while trying to locate the Temporal Shard and another before finding Kyrielee. Roll 1d6 to determine which encounter the characters stumble into, or just pick the ones you like the best.

Jonar has the option to join in if the skirmish seems to be turning against the party, but for the most part he looks on these encounters as tests to see if the group is strong and talented enough to accomplish the task he has set for them. He'll only help if they really need it. Remember, also,

that these encounters are intended to provide a distraction and reflect the natural ambiance of the deep dark forest, not to maim the party so badly that they can't continue.

1. DIGESTER

This dinosaur-like creature suddenly charges from the underbrush spraying acid in a 20-foot-wide cone as it goes. It follows this up with rake attacks, using its hind feet until it can try its acid attack again. If one character in particular does more damage to it than the others, the digester will choose to target that person for a concentrated acid stream.

The digester will attempt to flee if it is injured to the point of being near death. It has no treasure.

> **Digester:** SZ M (magical beast); HD 8d10+24; hp 68; Init +6; Spd 60 ft.; AC 17 (+2 Dex, +5 natural); Atk: rake +11 (1d8+4); Face 5 ft. X 5 ft.; Reach 5 ft.; SA acid spray; SQ scent, acid immunity; SV Fort +9, Ref +8, Will +3; Str 17, Dex 15, Con 17, Int 2, Wis 12, Cha 10; AL N. Feats: Alertness, Improved Initiative.
>
> *Acid Spray (Ex):* 4d8 damage to everything in 20' cone, or 8d8 versus a single target within 5' (Ref save, DC 17, for half damage); takes 1d4 rounds to "recharge."

2. PACK OF COMPSOGNATHUS DINOSAURS

A pack of 1d12+3 of these tiny dinausaurs lies in wait. They will wait until the party has passed them, then attack the last "straggler" of the group, converging on him much as a school of piranha might. When their number drops below four, those remaining will run away to hide in the underbrush. Although they have no treasure and their hides are too small to be worth anything, they are edible. Yes, they even taste like chicken.

NEW MONSTER:
Compsognathus

Tiny Dinosaur

Hit Dice:	1d12−1 (6 hp)
Initiative:	+3 (Dex)
Speed:	40 ft.
AC:	15 (+2 size, +3 Dex)
Attacks:	Bite +5 melee
Damage:	Bite 1d10−3
Face/Reach:	2 1/2 ft. by 2 1/2 ft./0 ft.
Special Qualities:	Scent
Saves:	Fort +1, Ref +5, Will +3
Abilities:	Str 6, Dex 16, Con 8, Int 2, Wis 12, Cha 7
Skills:	Balance +10, Hide +18, Move Silently +10, Listen +4, Spot +4
Feats:	Weapon Finesse (bite)
Climate/Terrain:	Any warm land
Organization:	Pack (4-15; roll 1d12+3 to determine pack size)
Challenge Rating:	1/3
Treasure:	None
Alignment:	Always Neutral

Compsognathus is a tiny, relatively intelligent carnivorous dinosaur that hunts in packs; its razor-sharp teeth make a bloody mess of its prey. It has a slender body 30 inches long and stands and walks on its hind legs. These creatures communicate with each other through small clicking sounds. Their small size and quickness allows individuals to remain hidden until the pack attacks.

3. SHRIEKER AND VIOLET FUNGUS

The party hears an eerie shrieking coming from a point about ten feet to their left. It sounds much like an injured cat or child. If they investigate this shrill noise, they come upon two human-sized purple mushrooms half-hidden in the underbrush. One of the fungi has four mobile tendrils with which it attacks the nearest character. The violet fungus doesn't have the coins, goods, or other items its previous meals might otherwise have left, because it is in a very remote location.

Shrieker: SZ M (plant); HD 2d8+2; hp 11; Init −5; Spd 0 ft.; AC 13 (+3 natural); Atk: none; Face 5 ft. X 5 ft.; Reach 0 ft.; SA shriek; SQ plant; SV Fort +4, Ref —, Will —; Str —, Dex —, Con 13, Int 1, Wis 2, Cha 1; AL N.

Shriek (Ex): Movement or light within 10 feet of the plant triggers a piercing sound that lasts 1d3 rounds.

Violet Fungus: SZ M (plant); HD 2d8+6; hp 15; Init −1; Spd 10 ft.; AC 13 (−1 Dex, +4 natural); Atk: 4 tentacles +3 (1d6+2 and poison); Face 5 ft. X 5 ft.; Reach 10 ft.; SQ plant; SV Fort +6, Ref −1, Will +0; Str 14, Dex 8, Con 16, Int 2, Wis 11, Cha 9; AL N.

Poison (Ex): The fungus' poison requires a Fort save DC 14, and deals initial and secondary damage of 1d4 temporary Strength and 1d4 temporary Consitution.

4. PAIR OF ASSASSIN VINES

As the party pushes through some dense underbrush, the characters may be attacked by two assassin vines.

Characters must make a Spot check DC 20 to notice the assassin vines along their path.

The plants are spaced about 15 feet apart, and each is concealed by the mass of mushrooms and other fungi that feed on its leavings. They both wait until their prey is in between them before striking. Since the reach of each plant is only five feet, there is a five-foot-wide space directly between the two that neither can reach.

However, if the characters attempt to use this space as a safe haven, the vines will animate the plants in this no man's land and drag the adventurers nearer. Both plants have bunches of small, grape-like fruits on them, which are edible.

> The exotic fruits would bring a price of about 1 gp per bunch. Roll 4d20 to determine how many of the fruits the party is able to recover, if they wish to.

Since these vines are far from any human settlement, they do not have the coins, goods, or other items normally found lying about from their previous meals.

> **Assassin Vine** (2): SZ L (plant); HD 4d8+12; hp 30; Init +0; Spd 0 ft.; AC 15 (–1 size, +6 natural); Atk: slam +7 (1d6+7); Face 5 ft. X 5 ft.; Reach 10 ft. (20 ft. with vine); SA entangle, improved grab, constrict 1d6+7; SQ camouflage, electricity immunity, cold and fire resistance 20, blindsight; SV Fort +7, Ref +1, Will +2; Str 20, Dex 10, Con 16, Int —, Wis 13, Cha 9; AL N.

Entangle (Su): It can animate plants up to 30 feet from itself as free action. As *entangle* spell cast by 4th-level druid (save DC 13).

Improved Grab (Ex): When it hits with a slam attack, it deals normal damage and tries to start a grapple as a free action. Each successful grapple check deals another 1d6+7 damage.

Constrict (Ex): After making a successful grapple check it crushes its victim, dealing 1d6+7 extra blugeoning damage. This is in addition to Improved Grab damage.

5. SABER-TOOTHED CAT

As they pass under a particularly large, low-hanging tree, a saber-toothed cat leaps down from its branches with a roar and pounces on the closest character. This large cat is approximately 10 feet long, weighs 600 pounds, and uses rake attacks to kill its prey. If it kills a character or renders him unconscious, the cat will attempt to drag the body away so as to enjoy its dinner at its own leisure.

> The hide of this cat would bring 200 gp at market, and its two large fangs can be sold for about 50 gp each.

> **Saber-toothed Cat:** SZ L (animal); HD 6d8+18; hp 45; Init +2 (Dex); Spd 40 ft.; AC 14 (–1 size, +2 Dex, +3 natural); Atk: 2 claws +9 (1d8+6), saber-toothed bite +4 (2d6+3); Face 5 ft. X 10 ft.; Reach 5 ft.; SA pounce, improved grab, rake 1d8+3; SQ scent; SV Fort +8, Ref +7, Will +3; Str 23, Dex 15, Con 17, Int 2, Wis 12, Cha 6; AL N. Skills: Balance +6, Hide +5 (+9 in heavy undergrowth), Listen +3, Move Silently +9, Spot +3, Swim +11.

Pounce (Ex): If it leaps at a victim during the first round of combat, it can make a full attack.

Improved Grab (Ex): When it hits with a claw or bite attack, it deals normal damage and tries to start a grapple as a free action. A successful grapple check allows it to rake.

Rake (Ex): If it can get a hold with Improved Grab, it makes two rake attacks (+9 melee) with it hind legs. If it pounces on a victim, it can also rake.

Once it is reduced to 10 hp, the cat will flee.

(Saber-toothed cat stats are as for a tiger.)

6. STIRGE SWARM

A low buzzing sound can be heard throughout the forest, growing louder and louder. Try as they might, the characters cannot pinpoint the location of this noise until the swarm of stirges is upon them. Roll 1d4+4 to determine swarm size. Distribute the stirges evenly among the characters. These bloodsuckers have no treasure.

> Each stirge will attack until it is either dead or has drained 4 Constitution points from the character it is attacking.

> **Stirge** (5-8): SZ T (beast); HD 1d10; hp 5; Init +4; Spd 10 ft., fly 40 ft.; AC 16 (+2 size, +4 Dex); Atk: touch +6 (1d3–4); Face 2 1/2 ft. X 1 1/2 ft.; Reach 0 ft.; SA attach, blood drain; SV Fort +2, Ref +6, Will +1; Str 3, Dex 19, Con 10, Int 1, Wis 12, Cha 6; AL N. Skills: Hide +14. Feats: Weapon Finesse (touch).

Attach (Ex): If the touch attack succeeds, the stirge latches onto its opponent's body. An attached stirge has AC 12.

Blood Drain (Ex): Once attached, the stirge drains a temporary 1d4 Con per round.

ILLUSTRATION BY DAVID INTERDONATO

RETRIEVING THE SHARD

When the characters reach the southwest corner of the lake, they find themselves at the top of a sheer cliff face which plunges straight down into the water below. The top of the cliff is about 100 feet above the surface of the lake.

A Climb skill check would work to navigate down the cliff to the spot about 60 feet down, where the Shard is located just out of reach of that 50-foot rope. However, a simple *levitate* spell, or a variety of other spells and magical items, can be used to accomplish the task of retrieving the Shard, as well. To avoid any surprises, the GM might want to look over his players' magic before beginning this section of the adventure.

An unaided Climb check would be DC 25 for this cliff, and movement would be possible at ½ the character's speed for each suc-

cessful Climb check. A Climb check of DC 15 can be used if the climber makes his own handholds and footholds using pitons, though it would take about 20 minutes to climb down the cliff this way, as movement is reduced to three feet per minute. A Climb check of DC 5 applies if the climber descends down a rope anchored at the top of the cliff. In lieu of having the climber make a Climb skill roll, a character at the top of cliff could lower another person down on a rope using sheer strength, but the climber can only weigh twice the stronger character's maximum load.

A failed climb check means no progress has been made. A Climb check that fails by five or more means the climber falls to the water below, though he can attempt to catch himself on a Climb check of the cliff's DC + 20 (though this isn't likely to happen). For the first 20 feet of the fall there is no damage; for the next 20 feet, he rolls 1d3 subdual damage per ten-foot increment; past 40 feet,

NEW WONDROUS ITEM:
The Temporal Shard

This item appears to be a large crystal about three inches long. When charged, a steady glow emanates from within the heart of the Shard. This is, in fact, a device that is able to collect or release one minute of time according to the wielder's will. As such, it can achieve the following spell-like effects:

Time Stop: For the bearer, all time seems to stop for one minute, except for him or herself. For observers, the bearer may seem to blink out of existence, and reappear instantaneously in another place. In effect, the Shard releases its charge to its bearer, imbuing him or her with a minute of time that the rest of the world doesn't experience. The bearer can move normally for that minute of apparent time, but is not able to influence anything stopped in time in any way; objects and people are immovable and impenetrable. The *time stop* spell-like effect counters *temporal stasis.*

Haste: For the bearer, all time seems to slow for two minutes, while he or she is left unaffected. For the observer, the bearer seems to move incredibly fast for one minute. In this instance, the Shard releases its charge progressively instead of in one burst, giving the bearer two minutes of time for every one the rest of the world experiences.

On his turn, the bearer gains a +4 haste bonus to AC, but loses it whenever he would lose a dodge bonus. He can also jump two times as far as normal, which counts as an enhancement bonus. All of the bearer's normal bodily functions — such as breathing, heart rate, death, etc. — occur at twice their normal speed In combat, it allows an extra partial action before or after a normal action. The *Haste* spell-like effect counters *slow.*

Temporal Stasis: For the bearer, one minute of time disappears. For the observer, the bearer seems to stop moving for one minute, entering a state of suspended animation where time ceases to flow and his condition becomes fixed. The empty Shard actually draws one minute of the bearer's time into itself, causing the bearer to appear to stop in time for one minute. During this time, the bearer is impen-

etrable by outside forces. The *temporal stasis* spell-like effect counters *time stop.*

Slow: For the bearer, all time seems to quicken for one minute. For the observer, the bearer seems to slow to a crawl for two minutes. Here, the Shard gathers up one minute of the bearer's time progressively rather than in one burst, reducing the bearer to one minute of time to the rest of the world's two. The bearer can only take a partial action every turn, and suffers –2 to AC, melee attack rolls, melee damage rolls, and Reflex saves. The bearer can jump only half as far as normal. All of the bearer's normal bodily functions — such as breathing, heart rate, death, etc. — occur at half their normal speed. The *slow* spell-like effect counters *haste.*

All of these effects include the bearer of the Temporal Shard, as well as anything within a range of three feet at the moment the crystal is activated, including other people. The activation time is instantaneous, and moving out of touch with the Shard after the initial moment of activation does not change the effect for the target(s). Because the Shard works based on charges, it can only be used in accordance with the charge it currently holds: if it is empty, it works to *slow* or induce *temporal stasis,* simultaneously drawing in a charge (a minute of time); if full, it can only cause *time stop* or *haste,* releasing its charge on activation. However, it can be used again for an opposing effect immediately following an activation.

Characters can tell if the Shard is charged by whether a glow emanates from it. When they first discover it, the Shard is not charged. Activation is triggered by a clearly formulated desire on the part of the wielder while the shard is in hand; the holder of the Shard then feels a slight lurch as his body is shifted into the new time frame. There is no saving throw and spell resistance doesn't protect others from the effects of the Shard, which are actually targeted at the bearer.

Caster Level: 17th; *Prerequisites:* Craft Wondrous Item, *haste, slow, time stop, temporal stasis; Market Price:* 300,000 gp; *Weight:* $1/_2$ lb.

he rolls 1d6 per additional ten feet of the fall. For instance, if the character fell from the location of the Shard 40 feet above the water, he would suffer 2d3 subdual damage.

Once he reaches the Shard, the climber must detach it from the overgrown mounting it was placed in so long ago. This might mean chipping the entire gold mounting bracket from its moorings in the rock, or somehow breaking the bracket, which forms a kind of cage around the Shard.

Either of these can be done with a Strength check at DC 17. The mounting has a Hardness of 5 and 1 hp. The heavy mounting bracket is itself worth 75 gp as scrap gold.

If things have been going too easily for the character climbing the cliff, you might want to add a little spice to this mid-air display of acrobatics. A hawk has made its nest about 30 feet down the cliff face, and comes spiraling down out of the sky shrieking its outrage when the climber disturbs its young.

The hawk gets a +2 bonus and the character loses any Dexterity bonus to his Armor Class because he is in the middle of climbing. If the character takes damage, he needs to make a Climb check against the DC of the cliff; failure means a fall, as described in the text above.

Hawk: SZ T (animal); HD 1d8; hp 4; Init +3; Spd 10 ft., fly 60 ft.; AC 17 (+2 size, +3 Dex, +2 natural); Atk: 2 claws +5 (1d4–2); Face 2 $\frac{1}{2}$ ft. X 2 $\frac{1}{2}$ ft.; Reach 0 ft.; SV Fort +2, Ref +5, Will +2; Str 6, Dex 17, Con 10, Int 2, Wis 14, Cha 6; AL N. Skills: Listen +6, Spot +6 (+14 in daylight). Feats: Weapon Finesse (claws).

There are two young hawks in the nest. These are pre-fledgling birds about $\frac{2}{3}$ the size of the adult female, and although they haven't learned to fly yet, they do have all of their adult feathers. They also have an appendage their mother didn't — each bears a lizard's tail instead of a hawk's normal plumage. They'd make very good familiars in a few weeks, or if

trained as hunting birds they'd fetch a price of about 200 gp each because of their odd mutation. That is, if someone in the group feels like playing "momma bird" until then, hunting small rodents and insects for the immature hawks. Otherwise, the female's mate will return to the nest soon enough and take over the care of their young.

When the Shard is retrieved, Jonar is happy to tell the characters about its power (or even before they go looking for it, if they question its importance to the adventure). If they get greedy and want to look for more Shards, Jonar tells them that this is the only one he knows of that was mounted on a distinguishable landmark that would have remained above water level — he wouldn't be able to find any of the others even if he wanted to.

CHARMING THE CHARMER

Kyrielee is a rather capricious water sprite, about four feet tall with webbed fingers and toes, pointed ears, and wide silver eyes. She has pale green, lightly scaled skin and dark green hair. She is wearing a wrap made of woven lake weeds, and is sitting on a large rock at the edge of the lake, playing with a piece of reed. Time variations have affected her as well as the surrounding woodlands, giving her abilities far beyond her actual years. This can make her dangerous despite her low hit points, but her gifts will be much to the party's advantage should they be able to win Kyrielee over to their side.

When they approach Kyrielee, she will immediately recognize Jonar and welcome him to her, calling him her "favorite big person." Jonar paved the way for the characters earlier by ingratiating himself to her before he conscripted the party to help him. The two have only met once before; Jonar looks on Kyrielee as being a means of saving his people, while Kyrielee sees him as no more than an amusement. There is no real bond here, but it's enough to keep Kyrielee from fleeing into the water the moment the PCs show themselves to her.

Kyrielee will quickly fixate on the character with the highest Charisma score (do not count Jonar for this, since he is already on her good side).

Kyrielee

Small Amorphous Nixie

Hit Dice:	4d6 (16 hp)
Initiative:	+7 (+3 Dex, +4 Improved Initiative)
Speed:	20 ft., swim 30 ft., swim 10 ft. in aqueous form (perfect)
AC:	14 (+1 size, +3 Dex)
Attacks:	Dagger +4 melee
Damage:	Dagger 1d4–2
Face/Reach:	5 ft. by 5 ft./5 ft.
Special Attacks:	Charm person, drown, kiss of water breathing
Special Qualities:	SR 16, aqueous form
Saves:	Fort +0, Ref +5, Will +3
Abilities:	Str 7, Dex 16, Con 11, Int 12, Wis 13, Cha 18
Skills:	Animal Empathy +7, Bluff +8, Craft (reed instruments) +5, Escape Artist +10, Handle Animal +8, Hide +10 (+15 when in water), Listen +7, Perform (dance, melody, and pan pipes) +7, Search +3, Sense Motive +7, Spot +7
Feats:	Dodge, Improved Initiative, Weapon Finesse (dagger)
Challenge Rating:	2
Alignment:	Neutral

Charm Person (Sp): Kyrielee will enter combat only to protect herself or her territory. She prefers to use *charm person* to win enemies over instead. She can *charm person* three times per day as the spell cast by a 4th-level sorcerer. Failing a Will save (DC 15) means the person will be *charmed* for 24 hours. A successful saving throw means Kyrielee's attempt to *charm* had no effect.

Drown (Sp): Kyrielee is able to *create water* as a targeted attack, filling her opponent's lungs with water and thus drowning him. She can use this attack three times per day as if a 4th-level sorcerer. Her victim is able to make a save vs. Will (DC 15); if this roll is failed, her opponent falls unconscious in the first round (0 hp), drops to –1 hp and is dying in the following round, and in the third round drowns. A successful saving throw deals 1d4 points of damage instead, and leaves the target incapacitated for five minutes as he coughs and sputters uncontrollably. Kyrielee can counter the effects of the drown attack by using kiss of *water breathing* on her victim, as described below.

Kiss of Water Breathing (Sp): The receiver of Kyrielee's kiss, when it is placed on his lips, is able to breathe water as the spell cast by a 6th-level sorcerer. She is able to use this ability up to six times per day (conveniently enough), and it also nullifies the negative effects of deep water on the subject, so that the character affected doesn't need to make Fortitude checks for damage due to water pressure. The effect lasts for one full day, but any attempt to save vs. Will negates it. Kyrielee is also able to breathe water herself as an extraordinary ability.

Aqueous Form (Ex): When Kyrielee touches water, she and all of her belongings melt into it, becoming water as well. This makes for an interesting effect when she dives into the lake. She is still sentient in her water form; the water that makes up her body is attracted to itself and is capable of independent thought and movement, though it cannot be injured by poison or critical hits any more than mundane water can (she also gains damage reduction 20/+1). She can maintain this form as long as she wishes while submerged in water. As she emerges from the water, she regains her solid form. Aqueous form is as the description of the spell *gaseous form*, with certain modifications; for instance, rather than flying, she is able to swim (speed ten feet, maneuverability perfect), though she is subject to currents. She can choose whether to use this ability or not, and she is not able to use her Spell-like Abilities while in aqueous form.

ILLUSTRATION BY DAVID INTERDONATO

She will talk only to this person, and will become upset if she is not flattered convincingly enough by him or her, or if others try to interrupt or talk to her directly. She is not above suggesting that she would look divine with that scrumptious gold bauble that the character wears encircling her own wrist, but prefers that others make the first move in paying tribute to her charms. Kyrielee might stimulate conversation with prompts such as the following:

"Those *persons* over there are very disruptive, glowering all the time … what was that you were just saying about the sunlight caressing my hair? And about my nice new bracelet being only a pale reflection of my own ethereal beauty?"

When he strikes on a line that the GM thinks is suitably flattering, Kyrielee's new favorite should roll a Bluff check (or Charisma) of DC 12. If all goes well, Kyrielee will be delighted by her favorite's courtly behavior and gifts. When sufficiently pleased, Kyrielee will give her favorite the

kiss of *water breathing* as reward and expression of her affection. Her attention then redirects to the character with the next-highest Charisma, and the dance begins again. If all of the characters win her over, she loses interest in them and dives into the lake, taking aqueous form.

When first approached Kyrielee will be immediately suspicious of anyone other than Jonar and her new favorite. This means she will become defensive if she feels threatened by their presence.

If she becomes upset, Kyrielee will first attempt to *charm* her favorite person, then use her other two *charms* on those who are making the most trouble for her. If this doesn't settle things down, or if she is attacked directly, she will use *drown* on the most openly hostile character, or on the one with the lowest Charisma if there are multiple belligerent persons in the group.

The use of these abilitis is designed to be a distraction so that Kyrielee can leap into the lake, using aqueous form to become a part of the lake itself, and thus invulnerable to the characters.

The GM can use Jonar to troubleshoot if things don't go well in this encounter. If someone fails his roll, Jonar can attempt to use *command* to force Kyrielee to give her kiss to him anyway. If she becomes upset and tries to use her drown ability, he can save her unfortunate victim with *dispel*

magic. If the characters try to attack Kyrielee, Jonar will attempt to forestall combat by restraining the most aggressive PCs with *hold person*. This should be enough to keep things on track, most likely.

Don't let the players rely on Jonar too heavily … this is a chance to roleplay, not to let an NPC take over the game.

The nixie will return to the shore once she is sure the characters are gone, or if they leave some kind of gift for her — preferably something pretty and shiny. She will only resurface if those who she found annoying keep their distance.

Perceptions Under Water

Deep water poses problems due to differences in visibility and in the speed of sound. Sunlight cannot penetrate water at all past a depth of 650 feet, and even at a depth of a twenty feet the world becomes very dim as particulates in the water diffuse the light. Non-burning lighting devices, such as sunrods or spells that create light, will come in handy, as even characters with low-light vision will have trouble seeing in the near-complete darkness of the temple interior. Ranges relating to light or vision should be halved to compensate for this difference: for example, sunrods only penetrate to a 15-foot radius instead of their normal 30 feet; Spot checks experience a –1 penalty per five feet of distance rather than the typical ten feet;

Search checks must also be within five feet of the object rather than the normal ten feet.

Sound travels four times as fast in water as in air; this makes it hard to tell the direction of noises, and makes underwater explosions especially dangerous due to hydrostatic shock from the concussion waves. At the GM's discretion, the sonic effect of explosions may be increased significantly; for example, a thunderstone might require a Fortitude save of DC 20 rather than its normal DC 15, and may cause physical damage of 1d4 or more. Also, Listen rolls should experience a +4 bonus to hear sounds, but a –4 penalty to locate their source due to directional ambiguities. Be sure to take this bonus into consideration when figuring Move Silently checks.

CHAPTER THREE

THE WATERS OF TIME

Before they begin the next section of the adventure, take a moment to have the players specifiy what equipment they'll be taking with them. Then figure out the characters' weight penalties (see page 27) and combat statistics based on these changes. It will make combat much easier to have this information worked out in advance. The inserts on pages 22, 27, and 28 also outline the D20 System rules for underwater combat, including some modifications specific to this adventure. Be sure you're familiar with these before beginning this chapter.

Before they enter the water, Jonar will offer to cast any spells he has remaining on characters who might benefit from them. After he finishes this, they are free to go in search of the temple of Ras'Tan. Jonar will try to follow the group as long as he can, but as soon as the sun isn't able to penetrate through the water Jonar cannot manifest himself any longer. He will begin fading as the light grows dimmer, until he is no longer visible. Though he is not manifested, Jonar will accompany the party from the ethereal plane.

> Jonar cannot make use of any of his spells, but he can still use *corrupting touch* to help the PCs with especially troublesome foes (at the GM's discretion), and may use *telekinesis* to help the characters find their way in the temple, even to the point of pushing someone in the direction he wants them to go.

MONSTERS OF THE DEEP

Before they reach the temple, the characters must navigate the murky depths of the lake. In addition to the danger of currents (described in the insert on page 27), fearsome creatures lurk below the lake's placid surface. Just as the characters start becoming at home in the water, a new foe appears to test their skill in underwater combat. The seepage of magical energy of the Temporal Crystal into the lake has spawned a multitude of anachronistic aquatic creatures as well as those the party encountered on land. An icthyosaur more than 30 feet long happens upon these strange, floundering creatures in the water, and moves in to investigate. Deciding they are in fact food, it attacks the characters.

TEMPLE OF TRAS'TAN

Stora

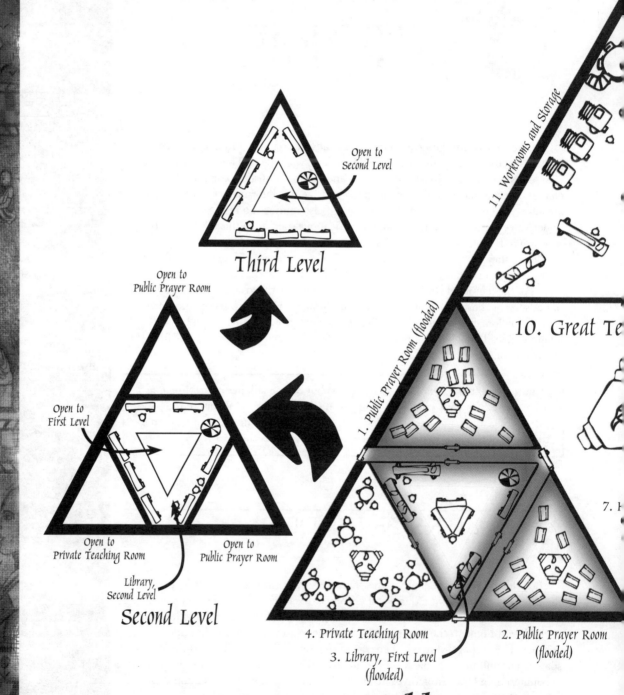

Third Level

Open to
Second Level

Open to
Public Prayer Room

Open to
First Level

Open to
Private Teaching Room

Open to
Public Prayer Room

Library,
Second Level

Second Level

11. Workrooms and Storage

1. Public Prayer Room (flooded)

10. Great Te

7. H

4. Private Teaching Room

3. Library, First Level
(flooded)

2. Public Prayer Room
(flooded)

Public Wing

ing

Scale

15'

45'

Second Level

Third Level

hamber

5. Junior Dormitory (flooded)

Junior Dormitory,
Second Level

ior Priests' Quarters
(flooded)

9. Kitchen (flooded)

8. Dining Hall
(flooded)

Head Priest's Quarters,
Second Level

Kitchen Storage

Open to
Dining Hall

Second Level

Priests' Wing

When the icthyosaur draws blood from one of the characters (or they from it), it attracts the attention of an even more fearsome creature. An elasmosaur, half again as long as the icthyosaur, swims into the fray. This effectively takes the fight out of the hands of the PCs, if they're smart, as both these behemoths turn their attention on each other, ignoring the puny characters in their fight for dominance. The two beasts will attack each other until one is dead, though the other will most likely also be incapacitated by that point, since they're fairly

ILLUSTRATION BY CHRIS SEAMAN

NEW MONSTER:

Icthyosaur

Huge Beast (Aquatic)

Hit Dice:	5d10+18 (48 hp)
Initiative:	+3 (Dex)
Speed:	swim 55 ft.
AC:	13 (−2 size, +3 Dex, +2 natural)
Attacks:	Bite +6 melee, Tail Slam +1 melee
Damage:	Bite 2d8+8, Tail Slam 1d8+4
Face/Reach:	10 ft. by 30 ft./10 ft.
Special Qualities:	Scent
Saves:	Fort +8, Ref +7, Will +1
Abilities:	Str 26, Dex 17, Con 19, Int 4, Wis 11, Cha 7
Skills:	Listen +3, Spot +6
Climate/Terrain:	Temperate or warm aquatic
Organization:	Solitary
Challenge Rating:	6
Treasure:	None
Alignment:	Neutral

The icthyosaur, though not a dinosaur, lives in the same aquatic habitat as they do. It resembles a enormous dolphin with four paddle-like flippers, a shark's tail and rows of razor-sharp teeth. It is over 30 feet long, weighing at least 4,000 pounds. When feeding, it uses its powerful tail as a second attack, striking out at anything behind it. Its speed and aggressiveness allow it to compete with other predators, and it will fight to the end for choice food.

evenly matched (flip a coin to decide the winner if you don't want to play out the entire combat scene). While they are both distracted, the characters have the opportunity to beat a hasty retreat, heading for the base of the pyramid before they're injured in this clash of titans.

> **Elasmosaur:** SZ H (aquatic beast); HD 5d10+25; hp 52; Init +2; Spd 20 ft., swim 50 ft.; AC 13 (−2 size, +2 Dex, +3 natural); Atk: bite +9 (2d8+12); Face 10 ft. X 20 ft.; Reach 10 ft.; SQ scent; SV Fort +9, Ref +6, Will +2; Str 26, Dex 14, Con 20, Int 2, Wis 13, Cha 9; AL N. Skills: Listen +2, Spot +5.

D20 System Underwater Movement & Combat

Swimming

A successful Swim (or Strength) check allows a character to swim at $1/4$ his normal speed as a move-equivalent action, or $1/2$ speed as a full-round action. The Swim skill is rolled each round at DC 10 for calm water, DC 15 for rough water, and DC 20 for stormy water. A failure means the character makes no progress through the water, while missing by 5 or more means the character begins to drown (although drowning is irrelevant for characters affected by Kyrielee's kiss of *water breathing*).

Swimming underwater accrues a −1 penalty to the Swim check for each round underwater due to the strain of holding your breath (although this penalty is waived if the character is benefiting from Kyrielee's kiss). A penalty of −1 is also taken for each five pounds of gear, instead of an armor check penalty. Fatigue damage is calculated every hour that a character swims; make a Swim check against DC 20 and take 1d6 points of subdual damage on a failed roll.

Fast-moving water or currents deal 1d3 subdual damage per round on a successful Swim or Strength check (DC 15). Impacting with things such as rocks causes 1d6 normal damage. On a failed check, the character makes another check to keep from going under.

Deep Water

Deep water also causes problems due to the increase in pressure. For every 33.9 feet of depth, one additional atmosphere of pressure (14.7 psi) is felt. This means that at a depth of 200 feet, the pressure would be 87 psi. Water pressure damage can be accounted for by applying 1d6 points of damage per minute for every 100 feet below the surface a character is swimming. A Fortitude save of DC 15, +1 for each previous check, staves off the damage. (The damage is also not applied if the character is under the influence of Kyrielee's kiss, although standard *water breathing* spells don't include this benefit.)

Cold water brings the danger of hypothermia with it. When swimming in cold water, characters take 1d6 points of subdual damage per minute of exposure. Luckily, the lake in this adventure is tolerably warm, so this problem shouldn't come into play.

Holding Your Breath & Drowning

A character can hold his breath for a number of rounds equal to twice his Constitution score in non-strenuous circumstances. Then the character starts making Constitution checks every round; the DC starts at 10 and increases by 1 each time. When the check is failed, he begins to drown: the character first falls unconscious (0 hp), next drops to −1 hp and is dying in the second round, and in the third round drowns. (In this adventure, Kyrielee's drown ability has these effects, but if all goes well drowning naturally will be made irrelevant by her kiss.)

APPROACHING THE TEMPLE

The temple itself is a triangular pyramid formed by three inclined walls — a tetrahedron — about 130 feet tall at its apex (imagine a gigantic four-sided die). The lake is 200 feet deep, leaving the tip of the pyramid 70 feet below the surface. The base of the pyramid is 180 feet to a side, and steps lead up each incline to the apex, at which is a triangular platform approximately 15 feet to a side. As mentioned earlier, the pyramid itself is an enormous sun clock, with the Temporal Crystal and its altar designed to be raised to the top platform during the day so as to redirect the sun's rays to a series of smaller crystals spaced at regular intervals around the base of the pyramid. These smaller crystals are located at a distance of about 200 feet from the top of the pyramid.

From their vantage at the top of the temple, then, priests were able to judge the time of day, season, and year — as well as taking more arcane temporal measurements — by interpreting the position of the light emanating from the Crystal. The Crystal and its altar were lowered into the Temporal Chamber at night using a system of hydraulic lifts, and a panel made of a stone-like material slid into place sealing the opening at the top of the pyramid.

The temple served yet another purpose as a solar collector. As the priests of Ras'Tan visited distant times in their pursuit of knowledge, they

GM's Underwater Checklist

For this adventure, it will be assumed that the characters are benefiting from Kyrielee's kiss of *water breathing*. This is designed to make things easier for GM and characters alike by not having to worry about things like pressure damage or drowning when skill checks fail. But to make play of this adventure into more than just unending Swim checks, some revisions are required. Use the following checklist when maneuvering underwater for this scenario:

Movement: Allow characters to swim at $1/2$ speed without making Swim or Strength checks during normal circumstances. Only require Swim rolls each round during stressful situations (i.e., combat), when PCs can move at $1/4$ their normal speed as a move-equivalent action, or $1/2$ speed as a full-round action. In this adventure, the lake is made up of calm water for the most part, which requires only a DC 10. However, if combat would likely cause turbulent water you may require a DC 15 roll. A failure means the PC makes no progress through the water.

Weapons: Bludgeoning weapons can be given a –6 attack penalty to factor in the water's resistance; slashing weapons experience a –3 penalty, while Piercing weapons hit as normal. For ranged weapons such as bows and javelins, their effective range is halved when used underwater. Slings do not function underwater, and they and some other weapons may be damaged by prolonged exposure to the water (see page 30).

Perceptions: Ranges relating to light or vision should be halved (Spot checks experience a –1 penalty per five feet of distance rather than the typical ten feet; Search checks must also be within five feet of the object rather than the normal ten feet). The sonic effect of explosions may be increased significantly and cause physical damage. Listen rolls should experience a +4 bonus to hear sounds, but a –4 penalty to locate their source due to directional ambiguities.

Weight Penalty: A penalty of –1 is taken for each five pounds of gear, instead of an armor check penalty.

Fatigue Damage: Every hour of game time have the players make a Swim check against DC 20 and take 1d6 points of subdual damage from fatigue on a failed roll.

Currents: Fortunately, the lake in this scenario is a rather placid body of water, with only occasional currents. Have the players roll 1d6 every so often to check for currents when swimming outside of the pyramid. A roll of 1 means the character has encountered a current which deals 1d3 subdual damage per round. Roll 1d4 to determine how many rounds he is trapped in it. He can escape before the current fizzles out by rolling a Swim check (DC 20) each round, as for stormy water.

ILLUSTRATION BY HELENA WICKBERG.

brought back a wealth of technological innovation as well as arcane knowledge. Rather than indiscriminately abusing their finds, and thus launching an industrial age that would traumatize the people of Lagueen and destroy their way of life, the priests were careful to dole out these advancements in ways that would only enhance the general quality of life. Technology was incorporated into the city in ways that fit unobtrusively into the people's lives and belief system. For instance, the great outer walls of the sun temple are covered with solar cells that caught the sun's rays and transformed them into enough energy for the entire city, as well as being a dazzling spectacle in itself.

As the characters swim down the height of the temple to its base, they should notice the flattened apex of the pyramid where the Crystal's altar was raised to catch the sun's rays. Because the theft occurred during the night when the altar was retracted, all the characters see now is a flat, stone-like surface at the top of the temple. No amount of effort will open it from the outside, as the mechanism to move the platform is located deep inside the bowels of the pyramid.

> The temple walls have a spell resistance of 30, Hardness of 8, 540 hit points, and DC of 50 to break.

By the time they reach the bottom of the lake, the PCs can glimpse the remains of the city laid out around the base of the temple. Peering through the murky water, they see the ghostly shapes of an ancient marketplace buried under several feet of dark silt. Vendor stands have been crushed under the weight of both water and years — all that is left are tattered and rotting cloth awnings waving in a stray current here and there, and several shattered boards jutting from the lake bed like tombstones. There's really nothing left to search through other than rubble and debris, and if they dally too long contemplating the treasures of the dead city, they may feel a shove toward the pyramid from their spectral companion. To gain access to the temple, the characters must either enter through one of the two entrances to the Public Wing, or use the Crystal Shard as an access key to the unobstructed door of the Priests' Wing.

Water Damage

The contents of any submerged room will have taken prolonged water damage, making them unusable due to rust or rot. However, those in "dry" chambers have a chance of being usable. After a character finds an item, roll 1d4 to determine its state:

1 = destroyed; the item crumbles in your hands as you touch it; the item is worthless from rot.

2 = severely damaged; either $2/3$ of the spells in a scroll are illegible (GM chooses those surviving) or the spellcaster has a 1 in 3 chance of being able to decipher a single spell (a roll of 4-6 on 1d6 is successful), potions have weakened and only work for $1/4$ their normal duration, weapons suffer −3 points to their damage, the Armor Class bonus for armor is reduced by 2 points, and other items have a −4 penalty to use effectively; the item is worth $1/4$ its normal value.

3 = moderately damaged; either $1/3$ of the spells in a scroll are illegible (GM chooses those surviving) or the spellcaster has a 2 in 3 chance of being able to decipher a single spell (a roll of 3-6 on 1d6 is successful), potions have weakened and only work for $1/2$ their normal duration, weapons suffer −1 point to their damage, the Armor Class bonus for armor is reduced by 1 point, and other items have a −2 penalty to use effectively; the item is worth $1/2$ its normal value.

4 = only slight damage; words on scrolls are still perfectly legible, preserved foodstuffs are still edible, and potions are fully functional; the item is worth its full value.

Remember that if damaged, a magic item will continue to function. However, if the roll determines that it has been destroyed, all its magical power is lost.

Also note that these rolls can be applied to anything the characters might have accidentally brought with them that can be damaged by water. For instance, the ink used in spell books may run, rations become soggy, wooden weapons warp, and leather armor swells. Because they will be in the water for a much shorter time than any of the treasure in the pyramid, though, modify the roll as follows:

A quick dunking — 1d4+3

Underwater for up to one hour — 1d4+2

Exposure to water up to one day — 1d4+1

Prolonged exposure, more than one day — 1d4

INSIDE THE PYRAMID

While from the outside the pyramid seems covered with large mirrored panels, from the inside the pyramid walls appear to be carved from one enormous white stone, with no joints or masonry apparent. This seamless expanse of flawless rock radiates heat or coolness into the interior of the temple, depending on the external temperature, to maintain a comfortable 72 degrees.

The main Crystal chamber is the full 130 feet height of the pyramid, while the other compartments are either 65 feet or 32.5 feet tall, and many are divided into multiple levels. See the map on pages 24-25 for the locations of the rooms described in this section.

When they enter, the characters will soon realize that breathable air has been trapped within many parts of the temple, and that the contents of those rooms are relatively intact. However, the priests did have time to secure the most valuable of the treasures of Lagueen before the destruction of their civilization overtook them, so most of the things left behind are either those too big to be removed, items too inconsequential to be missed, or things that were just overlooked.

A character can find one of these missed items if he makes a Search roll DC 15 in the appropriate room (i.e. the Library,

Laboratories, or Workroom; see pages 32, 34, and 35).

If the PCs miss too many items, feel free to use Jonar's telekinesis ability to make them more noticeable — for instance, it would be pretty hard to miss a previously hidden scroll hurtling through the air (or water) toward your head. However, the PCs should *not* be allowed to retrieve *all* the scrolls and potions listed in the room descriptions in working condition. This would unbalance the game horribly.

PUBLIC WING

The two outside doors to the Public Wing are already wide open, since they were made only to be closed during an emergency. They both open on a submerged corridor with archways opposite from each other half way down its length, and a large locked door at the end. There are temporal skids every 15 feet along the two main passageways (see page 39), and aquatic spiders infest several of the rooms in this wing (see pages 36-37).

This design allows a party to make it to the Great Temporal Chamber without exploring any other rooms, if they're really goal-oriented types; of course, the characters will miss all the temple's treasure going about it that way, and can be reminded of that if they don't think of it first. The larger intention behind this floorplan is to let the GM regulate the adventure based on how much time is left in the session. By adding impenetrable doors to the archways, this adventure can be reduced to one longer session rather than two.

1. PUBLIC PRAYER ROOM

This room was designed to be a smaller gathering room than the Great Temporal Chamber, for the general public to use as a common space of contemplation and meditation. Because of this, a curved archway leads into the room instead of a door. Originally, a Temporal Shard about 1/3 the size of the Temporal Crystal was seated in an elevated stone altar in the middle of the room, but this Crystal was hidden away by the last of the priests. There are kneeling pads positioned in a circle around the empty altar. The room is 32.5 feet tall, and the three walls are 45 feet long

each, tilting toward a point high above which makes a pyramid of the room itself (imagine being on the inside of that four-sided die). The Prayer Room is flooded except for a space about eight feet high at the upper apex of the room.

Decorating the walls are fabric hangings rotted through by water and time. Although the hangings crumble to the touch, those keeping their distance can see that they depict the daily lives of the people of Lagueen as they walk open marketplaces in the midst of their fellow citizens, enjoy the company of others in large garden spaces, and spend time as families in comfortable homes.

On a Search roll of DC 15, the characters might notice odd mechanical-looking devices in each of the wall hangings, apparently doing services for the people.

2. PUBLIC PRAYER ROOM

This is a mirror of the first Public Prayer Room, except that the crumbling wall decorations depict different scenes. These show the spiritual side of the people, rather than the harmony of personal interaction. In these, yellow-robed priests lead the devout in meditation, the religious kneel in a circle around a large glowing crystal, and in a view of a magnificent city a pyramid dominates the skyline as rays of light spill down from its apex.

A Search roll of DC 15 determines that the beams of light seem to be cast from a large crystal at the top of the pyramid, and that the rays end when they hit smaller crystals on the valley floor.

3. LIBRARY

The Library was another common space open to the public for study and meditation, and again two curved archways placed directly opposite of the entrances to the Public Prayer Rooms lead into it. The Library is a space 65 feet tall, and is the shape of an eight-sided die that is missing one side, so that the upper walls come to a point high above. It is much like being on the inside of a diamond set upside down (see side view on page 33). There are three levels to this room, with an iron staircase

Items in the Library

On the third level of the Library are useful items that may be recoverable despite water damage — after making a search roll DC 15 to find each item, roll 1d4 then consult the Water Damage chart on page 30 to see how well they have been preserved. Values show below are for objects with only slight damage. The items found include:

Scroll of *water breathing;* caster Level 5; worth 375 gp

Scroll of *bless;* caster Level 3; worth 25 gp

Scroll of *aid;* caster Level 4; worth 150 gp

Scroll of *prayer;* caster Level 5; worth 375 gp

Scroll of *restoration;* caster Level 6; worth 700 gp

Scroll of *divine power;* caster Level 6; worth 700 gp

Scroll of *freedom of movement;* caster Level 6; worth 700 gp

Scroll of *healing circle;* caster Level 6; worth 1,125 gp

Scroll of *bull's strength;* caster Level 4; worth 150 gp

Scroll of *endurance;* caster Level 4; worth 150 gp

Scroll of *cure light wounds;* caster Level 3; worth 25 gp

Scroll of *cure moderate wounds;* caster Level 4; worth 150 gp

5 unused **sunrods,** set in wall bracket mountings; 2 gp each

Magnifying glass; this glass has a carved ivory handle, with a piece of jade set in the end as a capstone, and gives +2 to Appraise checks for highly detailed items; 200 gp

Three inkpens; these are obviously writing tools made of polished mahogany, but the ink is somehow stored within the body of these odd devices. There is also some unusually thin and smooth parchment nearby, though it is yellowed and brittle from age; the inkpens are worth 10 gp each

Remember that if the characters attempt to bring the scrolls with them without somehow waterproofing them, they will be destroyed in the process.

---

connecting the ground level to second and third balcony levels. These upper levels wrap around the inside of the walls so as to encircle an empty central space. Every inch of wall space is covered with bookshelves and scroll racks, and there are work tables and chairs in the center of the lowest level. The Library is flooded up past the second level, but the third level has been spared.

4. PRIVATE TEACHING ROOM

Unlike the other rooms in this wing, there is a large, impenetrable stone door giving access to the Teaching Room (use the stats for the temple walls, given on page 29). It is locked, so that only the Crystal Shard can open it when placed in a crystal-shaped groove in the center of the door.

When the door is opened, a flood of water will rush into the formerly dry room, dragging the nearest PCs into the room with it. All characters within 15 feet of the door must make a successful Swim or Strength check (DC 15) to suffer 1d3 subdual damage (as if encountering a strong current). On a failed check, the character also needs to make another check or begin to drown if he is not using a *breathe water* spell (see the Holding Your Breath & Drowning insert on page 27). Making a DC 20 roll against stormy water will not allow a character to escape the drag of the water.

If the characters figure out a way into the room without opening the door, they will find that for the most part the water hasn't penetrated this room; though the floor does have a layer of shallow water covering it, the air within is breathable.

Crossection of the Temple

Great Temporal Chamber

Storage Wing (in back)

Library, 3 Levels (flooded)

Dining Hall (flooded)

Private Teaching Room

Kitchens

Public Wing

Priests' Wing

Public Prayer Room (flooded)

Senior Priests' Quarters (flooded)

This room is the same size and height as the Public Prayer Rooms, and has a similar stone altar in the center of the room designed to seat a missing crystal. However, this room was obviously used to train young members of the priesthood rather than being devoted to prayer and meditation. There are several small tables spaced throughout the room, and large frames on the walls contain a smooth, translucent material that has very neat writing imprinted upon it. The tenets of Ras'Tan are outlined on the boards, as if part of a memory exercise. There are also religious texts scattered on several tables, many of them duplicates of each other and well-used.

As in the Prayer Rooms, there are also several tapestries on the walls, these depicting the daily activities of the yellow-robed priests as they meet for a communal meal, study tomes of wisdom in the Library, and conduct a religious ceremony by encircling a ten-foot-tall crystal — the Temporal Crystal.

A Search roll against DC 15 notices that there seems to be a hierarchy in the priesthood made up of acolytes, junior priests, senior priests, and a head priest.

PRIESTS' WING

The two outside doors to the Priests' Wing were designed to open when a Crystal Shard is placed in the central groove designed for this, but are otherwise impenetrable (use the stats for the temple walls, given on page 29). They are made of the same stone-like material as the upper platform at the top of the pyramid. However, one side of the pyramid has taken an enormous amount of damage from a landslide that occurred during the original flooding of the valley, and the door on that side of the temple — the one nearest the Junior Dormitory — has been battered inward letting water into the Priest's Wing. That door is covered with boulders and silt, and so is no longer accessible.

This wing of the pyramid is suffused with a very dim light emanating from the walls of the temple. This allows characters to see as well as they would normally on a dark night, rather than halving the ranges for being in deep water. There are temporal lags every 25 feet along the two main passageways (see page 40), and tangle kelp has overgrown many of the rooms in this wing (see page 38).

5. JUNIOR DORMITORY

The Junior Dormitory is a 32.5-foot-tall pyramidal shape, the base of the walls being 45 feet each, and is divided into two levels. The lower level housed the acolytes; it has twelve beds and a tall cabinet for the belongings of each. The junior priests resided in the upper level, which can be gotten to via a staircase that leads to a much smaller area 27.5 feet to a side; there are six beds and cabinets in this space. The Junior Dormitory is flooded throughout the lower level, but the upper level has been left untouched. If the characters have the desire to look, they can find a few personal belongings left in the corners of the cabinets and underneath the beds — lost socks, discarded bits of paper or letters from home, and unmatched shoes make up the bulk of it.

6. SENIOR PRIEST'S QUARTERS

This section of the Priests' Wing has been divided up into three Senior Priest's Quarters and a central Head Priest's Quarters. Each of these is the private chamber of a high-ranking religious figure. The Senior Priests' Quarters are each pyramidal rooms 22.5 feet to a side and 16.25 feet tall. They have been cleared of most of their personal possessions, but each does still have a large bed and chest of drawers, a hardwood desk and chair, and a comfortable divan with a side table. Unfortunately, these three chambers have been flooded, so there is very little left for adventurers to plunder besides a few severely damaged works of Lagueen literature and religious philosophy left lying around.

7. HEAD PRIEST'S QUARTERS

The Head Priest's Quarters is a diamond-shaped room 32.5 feet tall, but divided into two levels with a central spiral staircase connecting them. Unlike the three Senior Priest's Quarters which encircle the Head Priest's Quarters, the second level of this chamber is still dry. Unfortunately, that level was reserved as a sleeping chamber rather than a study, so there is little but a very comfy, dry bed awaiting explorers.

8. DINING HALL

This enormous room is the same size and shape as the Library, but has an open ceiling stretching 65 feet above. Two archways open into it from the corridors, opposite the entrances to the living quarters. At one corner of the room is an ornate table slightly elevated above the others, with four seats arranged around it. A larger chair is positioned at the head. Immediately below the head table is a rectangular table seating six, and behind that is a long table seating 12. There are murals on the walls depicting religious scenes of the god Ras'Tan interacting with his people. The room is flooded about half way up its height.

Items in the Kitchens and Laboratories

The following items can be found in the Kitchens and Laboratories; after finding an item on a Search roll DC 15, roll 1d4 and compare the result to the Water Damage chart on page 30 to see how well they have been preserved. Prices given are for those items with only slight damage.

Potion of *swimming*; worth 150 gp

Potion of *water breathing*; caster Level 5; worth 750 gp

Potion of *cure light wounds*; caster Level 3; worth 50 gp

Potion of *restoration*; caster Level 6; worth 900 gp

Potion of *cure moderate wounds*; caster Level 4; worth 300 gp

Potion of *heroism*; worth 900 gp

Potion of *endurance*; caster Level 4; worth 300 gp

Alchemist's Fire; 1d4 flasks; worth 20 gp each

Acid; 2d4 flasks; worth 10 gp each

Sunrod-powered bullseye lantern; worth 20 gp

Rare spices; worth 100 gp

Alchemist's lab; worth 500 gp

Healer's kit; worth 50 gp

Items in the Workrooms and Storage Areas

The characters would most likely not know what to make of any of the slightly sinister-looking machines here. However, they may recognize the following items in the workshop area; roll Search DC 15 to find an item, then roll 1d4 and compare the result to the Water Damage chart on page 30 to see how well they have been preserved. Prices given are for those items with only slight damage.

Artisan's tools (metalworking), masterwork; worth 55 gp

Artisan's tools (woodworking), masterwork; worth 55 gp

Artisan's tools (leatherworking), masterwork; worth 55 gp

Goggles of Minute Seeing (wondrous item); worth 1,000 gp

9. KITCHENS AND LABORATORIES

Through the Dining Hall is the entrance to the Kitchens and Laboratories. This area was used both for the preparation of food and of potions. It is a pyramidal space 32.5 feet tall but divided into a main level and a storage loft. The loft is still above water and contains the normal contents of any food storage room; sacks of grain, preserved foodstuffs, and such. However, after more than a hundred years, the food stored here has gone far beyond putrid. The lower level has a food preparation area, as well as several spaces devoted to the working of magic.

Some useful or valuable items may be found in the kitchens and laboratories (see insert, p. 34).

THE HEART OF THE TEMPLE

10. GREAT TEMPORAL CHAMBER

The Temporal Chamber is the heart of the temple. This is a cathedral-like space 90 feet to a side, and is diamond-shaped. Sheer white, unadorned walls stretch up 130 feet to a triangular slab high above the chamber floor. Positioned at the apex of the pyramid, this slab was designed to keep out the elements when the altar was lowered into the chamber at night. However, the intense pressure focused on this point after so many years under water has caused tiny fractures to form in the joints. A narrow trickle of water falls steadily from that height, and has managed to flood the Temporal Chamber, over time, to a depth of about 35 feet.

Three locked doors lead into this room from the Public Wing, Priests' Wing, and Storage Wing. When opened, anyone within 15 feet of the two doors from the submerged corridors of the Public Wing or the Priest's Wing should take 1d3 damage (see the Private Teaching Room section on page 32 for a larger discussion of this). This new influx of water floods the room nearly half its total height — to a depth of about 65 feet.

In the center of the room is a grand triangular pedestal 15 feet to a side. On it is an immense carved altar with a ten-foot-tall glowing crystal prominently displayed. Lying near the foot of the crystal are two bloated bodies.

Upon close inspection (Search check DC 12), one can be identified as a young female wearing the remains of a yellow robe. She has a hideous expression of fear and horror on her twisted face. The other is much easier to identify (Search check DC10) — this body is the earthly remains of the priest Jonar, whose face is frozen in an expression of exquisite guilt.

A time elemental guards the Temporal Crystal (see page 41 for stats).

NEW MONSTER:
Monstrous Aquatic Spider

Medium-size Hunting Vermin

Hit Dice:	2d8+2 (11 hp)
Initiative:	+3 (Dex)
Speed:	30 ft., climb 20 ft. on land/20 ft, climb 15 ft. in water
AC:	14 (+3 Dex, +1 natural)
Attacks:	Bite +4 melee
Damage:	Bite 1d6 and poison
Face/Reach:	5 ft. by 5 ft./5 ft.
Special Attacks:	Poison, web
Special Qualities:	Vermin, blindsight
Saves:	Fort +4, Ref +3, Will +0
Abilities:	Str 11, Dex 17, Con 12, Int —, Wis 10, Cha 2
Skills:	Climb +12, Hide +10 (including +4 racial bonus; add +8 when using its web), Jump +6 (including +6 hunting racial bonus), Spot +15 (including +4 racial bonus; including +8 hunting racial bonus), Move Silently +0 (add +8 when using its web), Swim +8 (includes +8 racial bonus)
Climate/Terrain:	Temperate aquatic
Organization:	Solitary or colony (2–6)
Challenge Rating:	1
Treasure:	1/10 coins; 50% goods; 50% items
Alignment:	Neutral

Poison (Ex): The spider's poisonous bite can be resisted with a Fortitude save against DC 14; it has initial and secondary damage of 1d4 Str.

Web (Ex): The monstrous aquatic spider's web is specially adapted to its underwater home. It constructs a tightly woven, dome-like web along a flat surface in which it can store air so that the spiders can bring prey back to eat in comfort. Note that the aquatic spider can hold its breath up to a half hour, but then must return either to the surface of the lake or to its web or risk drowning. There is approximately five cubic feet of breathable air stored in the web, which can last one medium-sized character approximately 35 minutes. The web will be noticed on a Spot check of DC 20.

Vermin: Immune to mind-influencing effects, and darkvision up to 60 feet.

Blindsight (Ex): Using nonvisual senses, the spiders can detect creatures up to 60 feet. Invisibility and darkness are irrelevant, and it does not need to make Spot or Listen checks to detect these creatures.

The spider can also cast a web up to eight times per day as a net attack, to a maximum range of 25 feet underwater (50 feet on land). It is effective on targets up to one size smaller than the aquatic spider (i.e.. small creatures or characters). Prey can escape the web on a successful Escape Artist check of DC 20, or burst it on a successful Strength check of DC 26. A +5 bonus may be given if the trapped creature has something to walk on or grab hold of. Each five-foot section of web has 6 hp.

Each of these spiders is about five feet in diameter, including its legs; its body alone is approximately $1/3$ of that, and its torso is about six inches tall.

ILLUSTRATION BY CHRIS SEAMAN

STORAGE WING

11. WORKROOMS AND TEMPORAL ARTIFACTS STORAGE

Behind the Great Temporal Chamber lie the inner workings of the temple. Machinery used to regulate the temperature and air flow of the pyramid is located in this locked room. Although this area isn't flooded, the mechanisms have long since run down and are now still. This cavernous 90-foot-long, 65-foot-tall space has been divided into three levels so that it can also house large items brought back from other times. On the lowest level there are workspaces for activities such as forging magical items and tinkering with mechanical inventions, as well as experimenting with finds from other times.

> Be sure to give anyone within 15 feet of the door to the Storage Wing 1d3 damage when they open its door, as water from the Great Crystal Chamber rushes in. See the Private Teaching Room section on page 32 for a larger discussion of this. The Storage Wing will flood up to the second level, leaving the workshop area under water.

HAZARDS OF THE TEMPLE

No adventure would be complete without some difficulties on the way to fortune and glory. The following can complicate the characters' exploration of the pyramid.

AQUATIC SPIDERS

Throughout the Public Wing are infestations of monstrous aquatic spiders. Each web hosts from one to six spiders (roll 1d6 to determine the number; or choose this based on the party's overall level and condition at this point).

The spiders are territorial, so each submerged room will house only one colony; spiders are located in the two Public Prayer Rooms and the Library, but not in the locked Private Teaching Room. To scale these encounters up or down, use the normal stats for large- or small-sized spiders instead of those given here.

Should the players not trouble themselves with exploring these rooms, a few spiders might intercept them in the corridor. The creatures will then retreat into their own territory to draw the characters into deeper investigation of the temple.

TANGLE KELP

Portions of the Priests' Wing are overgrown with a fast-growing form of aquatic weed. It gained access to the temple when the landslide breached the door nearest the Junior Dormitory, and has moved into the Dormitory, as well as through the Dining Hall to the Kitchens and Laboratories. This poses a serious terrain hazard for PCs, both because the long fronds will slow their movement and obscure their vision, which may cause them to become lost, and because the kelp secretes a sticky entangling substance that can render them immobile.

The kelp reaches to the surface of the water in the hallways, Dormitory, and Kitchens, which will force PCs to struggle through it. However, clever players might note that in the Dining Hall they can just swim over the top of the plants. The GM might mention, however, that doing this leaves potential treasures hidden beneath the waving fronds.

NEW TRAP:
Tangle Kelp

This plant uses the dim light emanating from the walls in this section of the temple to stimulate photosynthesis, but must supplement this meager fare with a diet of small fish and water creatures caught in the sticky goop it secretes from pores along its strands. The substance immobilizes its prey and slowly digests it.

The tangle kelp is not a sentient creature, but poses a terrain hazard for PCs. The kelp has taken root in the silt that collected in the rooms nearest the landslide, and now forms a dense forest of leafy fronds gently waving as it trails upwards. Each plant is from 8 to 16 feet tall, and the largest plants form a heavy, goo-matted blanket on the surface of the water above, which takes a Strength check, DC 16, to push up through. Even with the description of the temple's floorplan given to the characters by Jonar, it would be easy to get lost in the chambers overgrown with this weed. Movement is reduced to $1/2$ because of this growth, and characters must make an Intuit Direction or Wilderness Lore check, DC 15, every ten feet they move to keep going in the correct direction. If a character fails this roll, he veers off either to the left or right of where he wanted to go; unless someone else corrects him, he won't notice his mistake. Characters who aren't tied together or staying very close to each other probably won't notice when one of their fellows wanders off, either. They need to succeed at a Spot check of DC 20 to become aware of their friend's problem.

When the players make their skill checks to keep from becoming lost, the GM should also roll 1d6. Rolling a 5 or 6 means that a character has become stuck in the goop the plant uses to catch its food. Roll randomly to decide which character is the lucky one. That PC is stuck as if with a tanglefoot bag; goop and fibrous plant bits entangle the character's body, becoming tough and resilient, and anchor to him more firmly the more he struggles. The character suffers a −2 attack penalty and a −4 Dexterity. He must make a Reflex save, DC 15, or be glued into immobility. With a successful save, he can only move at half his previous speed (that's $1/4$ speed, now, when combined with the $1/2$ speed penalty due to the heavy growth of the plants). He can break free with a Strength check, DC 27, or by dealing 15 points of damage to the goop with a slashing weapon, but then suffers the same penalty to his speed as if he had made the save. Hitting the goop is always automatic, but player characters still need to make a damage roll. Magic users must also make a Concentration check, DC 15, to cast spells while bound by the plants.

After ten minutes, the substance becomes brittle and is easily broken out of. No matter how a character manages to free himself, he always takes 2 hp of damage from the digestive acid of the goop by the time he cleans all it off of himself; this may only annoy PCs, but is enough to kill the small fish the kelp feeds on.

NEW TRAP:
Temporal Skids

A temporal skid is an area of sporadic time contained within another time frame — the time frame of the skid only exists for a fraction of a second in between time periods ranging from a minute to a century. Temporal skids generally take an oval shape about 2 1/2 feet along its longest axis, but with no depth. They hang in mid-air on their edge, forming a plane. Anyone breaking the plane appears to blink out of existence for an amount of time dependent on its caster level, then reappears for a fraction of a second, then blinks out again only to reappear later. The character doesn't have time to move away from the skid completely before he blinks back out of existence, and so will be trapped for ten leap periods before being able to eventually escape, unless he has outside help.

Like temporal lags, temporal skids are usually naturally created phenomena; they can be sensed by casting *detect temporal disturbance* and dispersed with *dispel temporal effect*. The caster level is used in a dispel roll, and also to determine the amount of time between leaps, as shown in the chart below. Temporal skids have a minimum caster level of 3, and the CR of the skid equals its caster level.

Caster Level	Period Between Time Leaps
3rd Level	3d20 seconds
4th Level	3d20 minutes
5th Level	2d12 hours
6th Level	1d6 days
7th Level	1d4 weeks
8th Level	1d12 months
9th Level	1d10 years

Take the period between leaps x 10 to determine the time needed for a trapped creature or character to escape by himself.

A rogue can notice the faintly luminous blur along the edges of a temporal skid on a Search check of DC 22. The temporal skids in the temple, which have a caster level of 4, are spaced about every ten feet along the two main passageways of the Public Wing (which means there are four in each hallway). These skids each have a period of from 3 to 60 minutes, which means that it would take a character anywhere from 30 minutes to ten hours to escape by himself. However, the Temporal Shard can free a trapped PC from this effect; if it can be put into his hand, he can activate the *temporal stasis* spell to freeze himself in time for two minutes the next time he appears. His fellows can then drag him out of the skid while he is frozen. But the character only has enough time to grab the Shard if it's waiting in the space that will be the palm of his hand when he comes back into existence.

This means another PC has to make a Intelligence ability check DC 18 to predict the location of the trapped adventurer's hand, then hold it there until he reappears. If he fails his roll, the victim isn't able to reach it in time because it's too far away. Have the PC who made the Intelligence check roll 1d4. On a 1, he managed to place it so that it actually occupies the same space as his friend's hand, which then takes 1d8 subdual damage. It will continue to deal this damage each time the trapped character blinks into existence if the Shard isn't moved.

Note that *haste* just doubles the fraction of a second the trapped PC is visible to the others — it's still not long enough to get out, or for anyone else to pull their comrade out. If a temporal affect other than *temporal stasis* is used within ten feet of a temporal skid, its period increases by a roll of 1d4 as the skid adds that energy to its own.

TIME TRAPS

The presence of the Temporal Crystal, which has been leaking massive amounts of temporal energy since its appearance in this time,

has caused several temporal instabilities within the pyramid. In particular, there are spots of temporal lag in the Priests' Wing of the temple, as well as temporal skids in the Public Wing.

If the players aren't able to figure out the trick of using the Shard to escape, feel free to use Jonar's telekinesis to make it more apparent.

NEW TRAP:
Temporal Lags

Temporal lags occur when the time frame of a certain section of space is moving drastically slower than the time frame outside of that space. In effect, this imbalance causes any creature or object that moves into the affected space to appear to slow until he or it gradually freezes in time (as if a *slow* spell slowed the target by vastly increased factor). Any other creature or object that follows the first into the temporal lag encounters the same effect, making this a kind of temporal quicksand. The depth to which a character — or object a character is pushing into the space — can penetrate before appearing to stop is dependent on the character's Wisdom. A character with a score of 1–9 will stop about one foot into the lag, 10–15 can move two feet in, 16–21 can go three feet, and 22+ can push in to a maximum of four feet. A character blundering into the area accidentally will stop at $1/2$ this distance.

The flow of time outside of the lag seems to swirl by at an insane rate for the person trapped inside. Though it seems to him that only a second has passed before he is able to make his way to the other side of the temporal disturbance, the time the rest of the world experienced may range from a few minutes to several decades. Temporal lags are usually natural phenomena, but they are affected by *dispel temporal effect*. For the purpose of making a dispel roll they have a caster level, which also determines the amount of external time that passes during that one second of time the victim experiences. Temporal lags have a minimum caster level of 3, and a CR equal to their caster level.

Caster Level	External Time to Escape
3rd Level	3d20 minutes
4th Level	2d12 hours
5th Level	1d6 days
6th Level	1d4 weeks
7th Level	1d12 months
8th Level	1d10 years
9th Level	1d10 x 10 years

These spots of imbalance are focused in the two main hallways of the Priests' Wing of the temple. There is one approximately every 15 feet (this means there are four in each hall-way), and they are the shape of a sphere about five feet in diameter. They each have a caster level of 3, which means that it would take a character from 3 to 60 minutes (roll 3d20) to escape by himself. On a Search check of DC 22, a rogue character may notice the fine particles of silt, or maybe even a small eyeless fish, suspended in a temporal lag. You may also want to leave one of the aquatic spiders suspended in a temporal lag as a warning of what's ahead.

Jonar isn't able to manifest within the temple, and so isn't able to use his *detect temporal disturbance*, *dispel temporal effect*, or *haste* spells to detect or disperse the temporal lags (nor the temporal skids, for that matter). However, the Temporal Shard can help. If the Shard is placed in the affected character's hand, he can trigger its *haste* effect to assist him in escaping, since that counters the effects of *slow* spells. The crystal's charge is limited to accelerating the user to two minutes for every one the area surrounding him experiences, though, so this would only reduce the time the character needs to escape by half. Others will notice that the trapped person seems to be moving faster if they try this.

However, anyone incautious enough to stick an appendage into a temporal lag for more than one second without following with the rest of his body is dealt 1d8 subdual damage from the disconnect between the two parts of himself; the appendage is paralyzed and numbed for 1d20 minutes, after which feeling comes back over the course of another 2d20 minutes as an ever-escalating sensation of pins and needles. The character suffers a –2 penalty to all skill rolls until feeling is restored due to the distraction and pain this causes.

Note that if a temporal affect other than *haste* is used within ten feet of a temporal lag, the external time needed to escape increases by a roll of 1d4 as the lag adds that energy to its own. If the players can't come up with their own solution, Jonar can use his telekinesis ability to move the Shard into the lag up to three feet with no damage to himself.

NEW MONSTER:
Time Elemental, Huge

Huge Elemental (Time)

Hit Dice:	16d8+64 (136 hp)
Initiative:	+11 (+7 Dex, +4 Improved Initiative)
Speed:	fly 50 ft. (perfect)
AC:	19 (−2 size, +7 Dex, +4 natural)
Attacks:	Slam +17/+12/+7 melee
Damage:	Slam 1d12+6 and *Hastening of Age* effects
Face/Reach:	10 ft. by 5 ft/15 ft.
Special Attacks:	Hastening of Age
Special Qualities:	Elemental, damage reduction 10/+2, time subtype
Saves:	Fort +9, Ref +17, Will +5
Abilities:	Str 18, Dex 25, Con 18, Int 6, Wis 11, Cha 11
Skills:	Listen +18, Spot +18
Feats:	Dodge, Improved Initiative, Mobility, Weapon Finesse (slam)
Climate/Terrain:	Any
Organization:	Solitary
Challenge Rating:	7
Treasure:	Great Temporal Crystal
Alignment:	Neutral

Elemental: Immune to poison, sleep, paralysis, and stunning. Not subject to critical hits.

Hastening of Age (**Sp**): As the new cleric spell on page 11. The time elemental is able to use this once per round as part of its slam attack. Creatures and humanoids affected by this suffer a reduction to their Strength, Constitution, and Dexterity ability scores. *Hastening of Age* can be dispelled by *Restoration*, but not *Lesser Restoration*; it is a permanent ability drain. *Wellspring of youth* can also counteract it. The effects of multiple hits are cumulative.

Time Subtype (**Ex**): The use of spells which manipulate time acts as an energy source for the elemental. Rather than affecting the elemental as it would other creatures, such a spell cast within 100 feet of it the spell imbues the elemental with 1d8 hit points +1 per caster level used for the spell, up to +5. These are permanent hp, which raise both the elemental's current hp and its maximum. Using the Temporal Shard will give the elemental 1d8+5 hp each time it's activated.

A time elemental will fight until it loses all of its hit points, and so no longer has enough temporal energy left to maintain itself.

ENTERING THE TEMPORAL CHAMBER

As the characters approach the Great Temporal Crystal and the two corpses laying at the foot of its altar, their last foe appears. The disturbance in the flow of time created by the presence of the Crystal has attracted a time elemental, which is determined to protect its source of power from intruders.

Time elementals are swift and agile. Their attack has the power to age a man beyond his years, and many an adventurer has returned from an encounter with a time elemental twice his previous age. A time elemental appears as a swirling mass of echoing darkness and blazing light given substance. Though huge-sized time

THE TIDE OF YEARS

ILLUSTRATION BY DAVID INTERDONATO

elementals such as this one reach 32 feet tall, they weigh nothing. Time elementals speak Temporal, though they rarely choose to do so. When one does, its voice sounds like the cry of lost souls through the ages.

At this point, Jonar will do his best to help the characters, engaging all-out in the battle to reclaim the Crystal for his people.

> Though still unable to manifest, he will use *corrupting touch* on the elemental for 1d4 damage at −1 to hit, and *telekinesis* to throw random bits of debris at the creature. *Telekinesis* used as a burst in this way requires an attack roll at +4 (Jonar's Attack Bonus), and he can find stone fragments large enough to do from 1d6 to 3d6 damage (GM's discretion).

Remember, though, that the characters' goal is simply to reach the Crystal and activate it so as to return it to its home time — if they can get past the time elemental without killing it, all the better for them.

CHAPTER FOUR

REPLACING THE TEMPORAL CRYSTAL

Once they get past the time elemental to the altar of the Temporal Crystal, any one of the characters can activate it by touching its surface and forming the clear desire to return it to its time of origin. Any attack on the Crystal, whether physical or magical, has no effect; the Crystal is the product of the combined will and energies of a thousand people. As such, it is a major artifact that contains a power beyond any one spellcaster or warrior's ability to influence. Any characters within 15 feet of the Crystal when it is activated are brought along with it into the past; their stomachs lurch as if a sack of gold pieces just hit them midriff, and the world around them revolves and tilts into a new perspective.

CHANGING THE PRESENT

In the present time frame, when the Crystal disappears the temporal effects it created wink out of existence; the time elemental disappears, as do the time traps, freeing anyone still inside a temporal lag or temporal skid. All of the damage to the pyramid caused by the decline and extinction of Lagueen is suddenly gone, and it is once again the center of a magnificent city in the heart of a wide river valley. Any characters left in this transformed present find themselves suddenly alone in the center of a now brightly-lit chamber, with the Crystal raised high on its platform to the top of the pyramid.

The PCs can easily walk out through the Public Wing of the temple without being noticed by the few citizens at worship in the Public Prayer Rooms. Should they choose instead to exit through the Storage Wing or the Priests' Wing, they will be taken for lost visitors by the priests, who will gently escort them back to the Public Wing without really paying much attention to their incoherent babbling — the devout, they know from experience, are sometimes overwhelmed by the experience of communion with Ras'Tan, and shouldn't always be taken literally. Nonetheless, the priests aren't able to explain the soggy state of the adventurers' clothing.

The characters then find themselves thrown out into the city's marketplace, which is filled with amazing gizmos and tantalizing foodstuffs. They have an entire-

ly new city to explore, and maybe even a sack full of treasure from the ruined temple that is no more.

REWRITING THE PAST

Those who are brought with the crystal to its home time find themselves suddenly in the same chamber, now devoid of any damage but dimly lighted by a soft glow emanating from the walls themselves. They have reappeared at the exact moment that the acolyte triggered the Crystal's leap forward in time. Horrified priests fill the room, but soon their look of terror turns to surprise and confusion. It's now up to the PCs to explain to the priests what happened, and convince them that they had no part in the Crystal's theft.

Meanwhile, if the corpses haven't been moved more than 15 feet from the Crystal, they too have been brought back with the PCs. Jonar, being an intelligent sort of ghost, made sure that he was also near the Crystal when it jumped back in time. He takes this opportunity to assert himself, throwing things about with telekinesis and generally making a ruckus so that his fellow priests will notice his presence. The characters may have realized that Jonar has been tagging along with them and try to tell the priests that the ghost is the spirit of one of their own. If not, one of the priests casts *detect undead* and comes to the same conclusion. The priests quickly wrap Jonar's body in a shroud and take him off to attempt to resurrect him.

Once they've convinced the priests of their good intentions, the characters are treated as all heroes should be. They're taken to the Dining Hall and wined and dined while their clothes are cleaned and mended.

If the characters are in need of medical attention, they are offered enough *cure* spells to heal completely. If one of their number died during the adventure, the GM may decide whether to allow the priests to *resurrect* that character if his body was transported, or *reincarnate* him if not. The GM may also let the priests cast *wellspring of youth* on a character to counteract the elemental's *hastening of age* effect.

The characters are soon told that Jonar is expected to make a good recovery from his ordeal, since he has been separated from his body for less then a day of experienced time. He is still weak and needs rest, but he was able to confirm their story when he regained consciousness.

Eventually, all good things must end. After extending their hospitality in grand fashion, the next day the priests tell the characters that they must return to their own time to finish making things right; the longer the PCs stay in the Lagueen of the past, the more likelihood there is that they might disrupt their own time. They are escorted out of the city in a procession befitting great heroes. The characters are then brought to the top of a hill outside of the city, and watch as the rays of light streaming out of the crystal at the pyramid's apex slowly move toward them. When the light finally surrounds

44

them, they feel a warmth and tingling throughout their bodies, as they are transported forward in time.

The forest surrounding them is suddenly a mature wood rather than the young saplings they were, and the characters look down upon a much larger city than was there before. Although the priests were unable to give them a reward that they could bring back with them without disturbing the flow of time, the PCs may still have a sack full of treasure from the ruined temple that is no more. And the city of Lagueen has a new legend of a group of heroes from the future who saved them all from the desolate tide of years.

REWARDS

If they took the time to search the temple, the characters should have a nice pile of loot by the end of this scenario. In addition, the chart on page 46 lists the experience points possible for each of the encounters in this adventure.

If you're not comfortable giving your players a magic item like the Crystal Shard, which has an enormous potential to be extremely annoying, feel free to have the priests of Ras'Tan reclaim it from the characters that are drawn into the past. It is *their* holy relic, after all. If you're feeling particularly nasty, the priests could go a step further and tell the characters that they can't take *any* of their found treasure back with them, for that matter, because having two of the same item exist in the same time period could cause catastrophic results. If the PCs end up with the Shard or too much treasure in their own time — whether by sneaking it along with them from the past or because they were left behind when the Crystal was triggered — the items from the ruined temple may just flash out of existence spontaneously, as the timeline rights itself naturally.

On the other hand, if you'd like to give your players a bit more of a reward, the head priest of Ras'Tan might offer to allow the characters to "take back" one event in each of their lives. Each character would, in effect, have this event and any impact it had on his statistics erased from history. Another approach to this option would be to make the "taking back" of each of these events into extensions to this adventure. Instead of just letting the characters skip over one incident in their lives, make them go back and prevent it from happening themselves.

Alternatively, perhaps the priests of Ras'Tan recognize the worthiness of the PCs and ask them to help gather knowledge from all the ages of history. Using the time traveling ability of Lagueen might then be a plausible way of taking a slight detour into the prehistoric past, or opening entirely new worlds for your players to explore.

LAGUEEN IN YOUR CAMPAIGN WORLD

If having an entire civilization pop up in the middle of nowhere doesn't quite fit into your carefully structured campaign world, there are a few ways to run this adventure without having to introduce Lagueen as a permanent fixture. In the first of these options, the priests of Ras'Tan can inform the characters that restoring the Crystal created a parallel timeline in which Lagueen still survives as a thriving nation, but that PCs' own time exists apart from that one. By taking this "parallel timeline" option, the priests are able to send the characters back to their own time, and timeline, without letting the rescue of Lagueen impact the PCs' world in any way. (That would also explain why the characters get to keep all the treasure from the ruined pyramid when the temple now paradoxically exists in their time in perfect repair.)

Another explanation for why the existence of Lagueen hasn't had an impact on your campaign world might be the isolationist philosophy they practice. Remember that the people of Lagueen believe in collecting information and technology through their manipulation of time, but they have also learned that expansionism and political strife with neighboring nations is the one sure way to plunge a civilization into decay. In this case, they make every attempt to keep outsiders from discovering them and the treasures they have access to. They may post mechanical sentinels and magical deterrents in the surrounding forest, designed to scare off intruders and the curious. This would lead to superstitions about the strange forces permeating the woods, and the ghostly dire animals wandering its overgrown paths, but otherwise it would keep the introduction of Lagueen from really changing the rest of your world.

Challenge Ratings & Experience

Listed below are the Challenge Ratings (or Encounter Levels if applicable) for each of the foes in this adventure, along with the experience points each is worth. Figure out the average level of your PCs, and add up the points under that column for each encounter they succeeded in defeating. Remember that "defeating" means being able to navigate past it to accomplish the larger goal; if they don't actually kill the time elemental, but instead manage to slip past it to activate the Temporal Crystal, that still counts as defeating it. Split the total experience points you come up with among your players.

Creature	CR (or EL)	4th Level XP	5th Level XP	6th Level XP
Jonar	10	None	None	None

(Killing Jonar does not gain the PCs experience points.)

Two (or more) of the following random encounters:

Creature	CR (or EL)	4th Level XP	5th Level XP	6th Level XP
Compsognathus Pack	¹/₃ each			
4-6 dinosaurs = EL 2		600	500	450
7-9 dinosaurs = EL 3		800	750	600
10-12 dinosaurs = EL 4		1,200	1,000	900
13-15 dinosaurs = EL 5		1,600	1,500	1,200
Two Assassin Vines	3 each = EL 5	1,600	1,500	1,200
Digester	6	2,400	2,250	1,800
Shrieker/Violet Fungus	1 + 3 = EL 4	1,200	1,000	900
Saber-toothed Cat	4	1,200	1,000	900
Stirge Swarm	¹/₂ each			
5-6 stirges = EL 3		800	750	600
7-8 stirges = EL 4		1,200	1,000	900

(Points are given only for killing the random encounter beasts — the few compsognathus who flee shouldn't be counted against the PCs.)

Creature	CR (or EL)	4th Level XP	5th Level XP	6th Level XP
Hawk	¹/₃	100	100	100

(This may be awarded to an individual if he dealt with the bird alone)

Kyrielee	2	600 (100 each)	500 (85 each)	450 (75 each)

(Experience points are awarded for charming Kyrielee, not for killing her. You can either give these points out to the whole group, or separately only to individuals who succeed in winning her kiss.)

Icthyosaur/Elasmosaur	6 + 5 = EL 7	3,200	3,000	2,700

(Either avoiding or killing the two beasts and making it to the pyramid earns XP.)

Aquatic Spiders	1 each			
1 spider = EL 1		300	300	300
2 spiders = EL 2		600	500	450
3 spiders = EL 3		800	750	600
4 spiders = EL 4		1,200	1,000	900
5 or 6 spiders = EL 5		1,600	1,500	1,200

(Points are given only for killing the spiders. PCs can earn cumulative points from multiple encounters — there are three infestations of these spiders.)

Tangle Kelp	2 per room	600	500	450

(Points are given for successfully navigating a room to reach a designated target. The kelp has overgrown three rooms.)

Four Temporal Lags	3 each = EL 7	3,200	3,000	2,700

(Points are awarded to the group if they avoid the traps or rescue their fellows rather than leaving them behind.)

Four Temporal Skids	4 each = EL 8	4,800	4,500	3,600

(Points are awarded to the group if they avoid the traps or rescue their fellows rather than leaving them behind.)

Time Elemental	7	3,200	3,000	2,700

(Either avoiding or killing the time elemental earns XP.)

Returning the Crystal	None	1,200	1,000	900

(Activation of the Crystal in order to send it home counts for XP.)

Typical Total Group XP

4th Level = 24,000 XP (4,800 XP each player*)
5th Level = 22,000 XP (4,400 XP each player*)
6th Level = 18,900 XP (3,780 XP each player*)

*Individual player XP assumes a group of five players

Taking this second option to the extreme, perhaps the priests of Lagueen decide that the only way to protect themselves is to move the entire river valley to an alternate plane. Or maybe they use their control of time to cast a time skip of massive proportions on their own valley; this would cause Lagueen to skip through time, spending only one day in real time every hundred years the outside world experiences. Either of these plans would keep the valley out of reach of envious borderland warlords, and would minimize Lagueen's impact on your campaign world.

If you do decide to add Lagueen to your campaign, there are a few questions you might want to consider. First, how has the centuries-long existence of a technologically advanced civilization impacted the other inhabitants of your world? Are there grand caravan roads where once there was only a narrow path through an uninhabited woods? Does everyone now use strange new gizmos — or even weapons stronger than magic — where once the ways of mechanical invention were the sole jurisdiction of the gnomes? How does the changed timeline impact the characters individually? Are their families and friends still as they left them? And are the characters themselves still *who* they were originally, or have their life histories changed as well as the world around them? Of course, you can always say that nothing has really changed, but working through these questions might yield the seeds for another adventure in itself, as the characters now explore a world subtly (or drastically) unlike the one they left!

OPEN GAME LICENSE
Version 1.0

Product Order Form

Mail orders to Atlas Games, Attn: Mail Order, PO Box 131233, Roseville, MN 55113, USA. Credit Card orders may be faxed to 651-638-0084. Questions? Write the above address, call us at 651-638-0077, e-mail us at info@atlas-games.com, or consult our web site at www.atlas-games.com.

Card, Board, and Button Games

_____	AG1001	Once Upon A Time, 2nd Edition	18.95
_____	AG1100	Lunch Money	18.95
_____	AG1200	Spammers	24.95
_____	AG1210	Cults Across America	44.95
_____	AG1220	Corruption	18.95
_____	AG1230	Letter Head	19.95
_____	AG3331	Prudence & Charity Lunch Money Button Men	4.50
_____	AG3332	Faith & Temperence Lunch Money Button Men	4.50
_____	AG3333	Hope and Chastity Lunch Money Button Men	4.50

Penumbra™ D20 Adventures

_____	AG3200	Three Days to Kill	8.95
O/P	AG3201	Thieves in the Forest RECENTLY OUT OF PRINT	8.95
_____	AG3202	In the Belly of the Beast	8.95
_____	AG3203	The Tide of Years	10.95
_____	AG3204	Touched by the Gods (Hardcover) AVAILABLE MAY 2001	23.95

Unknown Armies RPG

_____	AG6000	Unknown Armies RPG	25.00
_____	AG6001	One Shots	14.95
_____	AG6002	Lawyers, Guns and Money	19.95
_____	AG6003	Postmodern Magick	23.95
_____	AG6004	Statosphere	19.95
_____	AG6005	Hush Hush	19.95
_____	AG6006	Pain's Fair Price AVAILABLE JUNE 2001	tba

Feng Shui RPG

_____	AG4000	Feng Shui RPG	30.00
_____	AG4001	Seed of the New Flesh	19.95
_____	AG4002	Golden Comeback	19.95
_____	AG4003	Elevator to the Netherworld	19.95
_____	AG4004	Four Bastards	8.95
_____	AG4005	Seal of the Wheel	19.95
_____	AG4006	In Your Face Again AVAILABLE APRIL 2001	19.95

Ars Magica RPG

_____	AG0204	Ars Magica 4th Edition RPG (Softcover)	29.95
_____	AG0204HC	Ars Magica 4th Edition RPG (Hardcover)	45.00
_____	AG0255	Kabbalah: The Mysteries of Judaism	21.95
_____	AG0258	The Wizard's Grimoire, Revised Edition	22.95
_____	AG1110	Faeries: Revised Edition	17.00
_____	AG1120	Houses of Hermes	17.00
_____	AG0251	Parma Fabula: Storyguide Screen	14.95
_____	AG0254	A Medieval Tapestry	21.95
_____	AG0256	Return of the Stormrider	14.95
_____	AG0257	Festival of the Damned	17.95
_____	AG0259	The Mythic Seas	16.95
_____	AG0260	The Dragon and the Bear	23.95
_____	AG0261	Ultima Thule: Mythic Scandinavia	20.95
_____	AG0262	Heirs to Merlin	22.95
_____	AG0263	Ordo Nobilis: Mythic Europe's Nobility	25.95
_____	AG0264	Triamore: The Covenant at Lucien's Folly	20.95
_____	AG0265	The Mysteries	21.95
_____	AG0266	The Medieval Bestiary	19.95
_____	AG0500	A Midsummer Night's Dream	12.00
_____	AG0502	A Winter's Tale	12.95
_____	AG0503	Twelfth Night	12.00
_____	AG0600	Mythic Europe	18.00
_____	AG0750	Tribunals of Hermes: Iberia	12.00
_____	AG0751	Tribunals of Hermes: Rome	12.00
_____	AG0802	The Stormrider	9.95
_____	AG0811	Deadly Legacy	12.00
_____	AG0812	Pact of Pasaquine	12.95
_____	AG0813	Black Death	12.95
_____	AG0902	Mistridge	12.00
_____	AG1016	Mythic Places	9.95
_____	AG1018	More Mythic Places	9.95
_____	AG1150	Lion of the North	14.95
_____	AG1500	Medieval Handbook	20.00
_____	AG3020	The Sorceror's Slave	7.95
_____	AG3025	Trial by Fire	7.95

Furry Pirates RPG

_____	AG3100	Furry Pirates RPG	22.95

Over the Edge RPG

_____	AG2002	Over the Edge 2nd Edition RPG	25.00
_____	AG2010	Player's Survival Guide	10.00
_____	AG2100	New Faces	4.95
_____	AG2101	Airwaves	4.95
_____	AG2102	House Call	4.95
_____	AG2103	Unauthorized Broadcast	4.95
_____	AG2104	It Waits...	4.95
_____	AG2151	Forgotten Lives	19.95
_____	AG2200	Welcome to Sylvan Pines	8.00
_____	AG2201	With a Long Spoon	8.95
_____	AG2300	Wildest Dreams	10.95
_____	AG2301	Weather the Cuckoo Likes	12.95
_____	AG2302	Friend or Foe	10.95
_____	AG2303	Cloaks: The Sourcebook of Secret Agents	17.95
_____	AG2402	EdgeWork Fanzine #2	5.95
_____	AG2403	EdgeWork Fanzine #3	5.95
_____	AG2404	EdgeWork Fanzine #4	5.95

On the Edge Collectible Card Game

_____	AG2505	On the Edge Std. Starter Disp.	15.00
_____	AG2515	On the Edge Std. Booster Disp.	20.00
_____	AG2521	The Cut-Ups Project Booster Disp.	20.00
_____	AG2523	Shadows Expansion Booster Disp.	20.00
_____	AG2527	Arcana Expansion Booster Disp.	20.00
_____	AG2528	Burger Box Mixed Disp.	25.00
_____	AG2600	Surviving On the Edge	9.95

Cyberpunk 2020 Licensed Scenarios

_____	AG5005	Night City Stories	15.00
_____	AG5010	Osiris Chip	8.00
_____	AG5020	Streefighting	10.00
_____	AG5025	Chrome Berets	12.00
_____	AG5035	Chasing the Dragon	9.95
_____	AG5040	All Fall Down!	8.00
_____	AG5045	Thicker Than Blood	9.00
_____	AG5050	The Bonin Horse	7.95
_____	AG5055	Greenwar	12.00
_____	AG5065	Cabin Fever	8.95
_____	AG5070	Northwest Passage	10.00

Other Titles

_____	AG2700	Pierced Heart (Over the Edge Novel)	14.95
_____	AG2701	The Rough and the Smooth (Hardcover Novel)	25.00
_____	AG2917	Blood Nativity (Vampire: the Masquerade Scenario)	4.99
_____	AG5400	Hell Bent (Underground Scenario)	8.95

Sub-Total _____

Shipping and Handling (see below) _____

Total Price _____

SHIPPING INFORMATION

Name _____

Address _____

_____

E-Mail _____

Phone _____

PAYMENT TYPE

____ Check (payable to Atlas Games)

____ Money Order

____ Credit Card

    Circle One: Visa, Mastercard, American Express, Discover

    Number_____

    Expires _____

    Signature_____

Shipping and Handling

United States: $5.00 per order. Canada: $6.00 per order or $2.00 per item, whichever is greater. All other locations: 125% of actual shipping cost. Call or e-mail for quote.

Prices and availability current February 2001